MOVING FORWARD

BY

HENRY FORD

IN COLLABORATION WITH

SAMUEL CROWTHER

LONDON
WILLIAM HEINEMANN LTD

FIRST PUBLISHED 1931

C 1041193 3

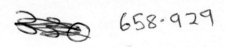 658·929

PRINTED
IN GT. BRITAIN AT
THE WINDMILL PRESS

TABLE OF CONTENTS

CHAPTER | | PAGE
I	THE WAY TO WEALTH	1
II	THE FEAR OF OVERPRODUCTION	16
III	LABOUR SERVING OR LABOUR SAVING?	32
IV	THE PLACE OF WAGES	44
V	UNEMPLOYMENT OR LEISURE?	62
VI	THE VALUE OF LEISURE	80
VII	THE PROBLEM OF AGE	89
VIII	TOWARD ABOLISHING POVERTY	100
IX	THE NEW CRAFTSMANSHIP	120
X	MANAGEMENT AND SIZE	139
XI	CHANGING OVER AN INDUSTRY	158
XII	FLEXIBLE MASS PRODUCTION	170
XIII	THE CHANGING SCENE	187
XIV	A MILLIONTH OF AN INCH	203
XV	THE STORY OF 199 SHIPS	220
XVI	TAKING THE METHODS OVERSEAS	242
XVII	THE WORK ABROAD	252
XVIII	EDUCATION FOR LEADERSHIP	266
XIX	PROHIBITION OR POVERTY?	280
XX	MOVING FORWARD	292
XXI	THE LIMITS OF MONEY	304

MOVING FORWARD

CHAPTER I

THE WAY TO WEALTH

I S IT possible that this country is losing its business bearings? There is talk of high wages being a burden, of raising prices to cover increased costs of production due to low demand, of curtailing output by agreement in order to prevent the country being flooded with goods, and even of passing laws to cure unemployment.

If wages are at all generally cut, if prices are raised and if production is rationed by agreement so that all the manufacturers in each branch of industry may have a certain amount of business regardless of whether or not they deserve it, then we might as well close the book of American progress. For business will have confessed its inability to provide leaders who can lead toward a greater and more widely diffused prosperity that will abolish poverty.

That would be a sad ending to our national progress. It is, however, an inevitable ending if the business of the country refuses to recognize its responsibility and hopes by catchwords and slogans to achieve that which can be attained only by hard, unremitting thought and hard, unremitting work.

Good business, which in turn means general prosperity and employment, is not something which comes about by chance. It is a result of the skill with which business in

general is managed—and business in general is only the
sum of the activities of the business units. Through all
the years that I have been in business I have never yet
found our business bad as a result of any outside force.
It has always been due to some defect in our own company, and whenever we located and repaired that defect
our business became good again—regardless of what anyone else might be doing. And it will always be found that
this country has nationally bad business when business
men are drifting, and that business is good when men take
hold of their own affairs, put leadership into them, and
push forward in spite of obstacles. Only disaster can result when the fundamental principles of business are disregarded and what looks like the easiest way is taken.
These fundamentals, as I see them, are:

(1) To make an ever-increasingly large quantity of
goods of the best possible quality, to make them in the
best and most economical fashion, and to force them
out on the market.

(2) To strive always for higher quality and lower
prices as well as lower costs.

(3) To raise wages gradually but continuously—and
never to cut them.

(4) To get the goods to the consumer in the most
economical manner so that the benefits of low-cost production may reach him.

These fundamentals are all summed up in the single
word "service" but that word is so often used just to cover
cheap and easy gestures involving no thought or work,
that it is necessary to point out that service, to be anything at all, must be the basic policy of a business and

must carry through its every action. The service starts with discovering what people need and then supplying that need according to the principles that have just been given. One must keep ahead of the needs of the people and not sit around simply filling what is called a demand. That is what I mean by leadership. When leadership slackens, then business slackens and the business begins to run the managers instead of the managers running the business.

Whenever the leaders of business find the public buying eagerly, the tendency is to settle back on the job and let well enough alone. There was formerly a tendency in such times to raise prices in the hope of getting in all possible amounts of money while the going was good. In consequence, in what were called times of good business, the effort was not to keep business good but to get money quickly, and since raising prices always seems to be the quickest way of getting money, the prices were raised and raised until they went above the level of the buying power, and then all at once the buying would stop and, instead of good business, we had bad business. Fortunately, most men have now learned the fallacy of trying to make money by raising prices, and we had little or no price raising in the period of our business history that terminated in the stock-market panic of October and November of 1929.

At the beginning of the period of speculation, the business of the country was running along very nicely and evenly, with the sole expectation of gaining profit through work, which in the end is the only way that any profit can be gained. Men kept trying for lower prices and higher wages—that is, to establish sound and enduring business.

Then, as the opportunities for making money in the stock market appeared, more and more the attention of many of the men who had been leading business and many of the men who had been helping them and many of the men who had been working for them became diverted to speculation. It reminded me of the farmers when the city was expanding and real-estate agents were subdividing outlying fields. The farmers kept one eye on the look-out for a real-estate agent and the other on the plow. It was very bad for farming. One eye on business and the other on the stock market proved very bad for business.

The proper conduct of a business requires every ounce of leadership that it is possible to exert. There can be no let-up and no attention to anything else. But inevitably this attention to the stock market drew attention away from business and dulled the edge of the urge always to advance. Customers were too easy to get and to keep, and business in general, instead of trying to make better products, sought to attain a greater volume of products and not to bother much with price reductions or wage increases. Everything was going so smoothly that there seemed no reason for undue disturbance or alarm. The true occasion for alarm was deeply hid. It consisted in the complete stoppage of improvement in quality of goods and in methods of manufacture, which in turn causes a stoppage in the increasing values of the purchasing money. There is bound to come a time when things are offered for sale at so much more than they are worth that the public will hesitate to buy them, and then will stop buying altogether and may even fall into a panic about what it has bought. I do not know anything at all about stocks.

But I do know that the manufacturing of stocks can be carried on in much the same way as the manufacture of articles, and their prices can be run up in the same way as commodity prices and with the same eventual result. Shoddy stocks can be made to sell at high prices.

The lesson that should be apparent from all this is that in the end everybody is the loser and no one the gainer by speculating in things already made—whether those things be commodities or whether they be paper shares in corporations. Prosperity and progress are in things yet to be made. Another lesson is that nothing can be taken for granted in business. If a business be allowed to run on as it is, just because the output is being bought, and no attempt is made to improve either the output or its method of making or to lower prices, then one day it will be discovered that there are no buyers. Every business, if it expects to be prosperous, has to keep ahead of the public. It cannot simply travel along.

If the nation's recent experience will have taught the lesson that no money is to be made except out of service, then it will have been worth all that it cost. The country needed some such education on a large scale as a step toward that kind of business which elevates the whole country and not just a few people. We may have been helped toward the view that goods and services are seldom luxuries, that it is nonsense to talk about people being better off with less, and that the only real luxury is a retired business man. For a part of the troubles which are said to be due to overproduction are really due to the habit of thought that a man has a station in life, and that too much in the way of goods and services may not be good for him—that he must be guarded against extravagance not by education but by withholding goods and money from him. There may be a personal nobility in poverty but it is a class distinction that we can do without.

Undoubtedly there are defects in the money system which sometimes prevent the free flow of goods and services, but we do not as yet seem to know enough to put our fingers on what exactly are the defects. We do know that periods arrive in which people in general, although their needs keep constantly increasing, have not the money to buy that which will satisfy their needs. There is no logical reason why, with ample facilities for production and an always increasing desire for consumption, there should at any time be one of these periods in which the desires cannot be fulfilled and the production utilized simply through lack of money. In fact, is it proper ever to say "lack of money"? Is it not fundamentally lack of something else? Money is like any other kind of machinery —it can be improved and is being improved constantly. But along with the machinery must come an instructed people that can properly operate it. Money, as we often say here, is like coal out in the big coal pile at the back of the shops. But what kind of management is it that fails to replenish it? The country has just had a clear lesson that money is a by-product of industry. When we give our entire attention to its sources—that is, to industry—there is no lack of money. The money market or the stock market did not cause the recent experience of business. It was men's neglect of business that upset the stock market. Business is the source of supply and surplus. Even a stock market cannot afford to neglect it.

No one has yet been born who can manage both to manipulate the market for its stock and also to do business in such a way that it will be profitable. The two do not and cannot mix. We have had acutely brought home to us what it means to have a considerable portion of the country take its mind off doing business and engage in a career of speculating in stocks.

The immediate cure for depression, and by depression I mean a period when men are out of work and not able to improve their standards of living, is told in one word, "quantity"—quantities of goods pushed out into the world.

But it is not enough simply to manufacture goods. There is a great deal more to the process than that. There is no service in simply setting up a machine or a plant and letting it turn out goods. The service extends into every detail of the design, the making, the wages paid, and the selling price. None of these can ever be taken as right—they can only represent the best efforts of the moment. That is why quantity production demands so much more leadership than did the old production. Anyone who sets up a big plant to manufacture a product and then takes for granted that no further changes in design or materials or methods of making are necessary will in a curiously short space of time discover an overproduction and then the owners will start talking about the market being saturated.

A market is never saturated with a good product, but it is very quickly saturated with a bad one, and no matter how good anything may be when it is first produced it will not remain good unless its standard is constantly improved. This does not mean that new and startling changes should be made every little while, for that is not possible in a product that began by being as good as it could be made. It is not necessarily good business to announce every change. The good will of the public is secured by quietly pressing for changes which will keep the product constantly more satisfactory, for then the reputation of the commodity will be simply that it always meets the buyer's needs. The public rarely asks for changes. But the public itself unconsciously changes, and a uniformly satisfactory article is one made by a management that is always pressing to improve it.

The right sales price is always the lowest price at which, all things considered, the article can be manufactured, and since experience in making and volume of sales will bring about lower costs, the sales price can as a rule constantly be lowered. It is the duty of a manufacturer constantly to lower prices and increase wages. The duty is not only to the public. A manufacturer owes this procedure to himself, for not otherwise can he control his business. There seems to be a good deal of misunderstanding on this point.

Lowering a price will generally increase business, if it is not a defensive act but a progressive movement. There are a great many strata of buying power and they are not sharply separated. They seem to vary almost from day to day, and even a slight change of price may take one into a new buying territory that has never before been explored. The reduction in price may not always be in dollars. It may be in added quality—that is, in giving more for the money. The very best reductions are those which comprehend both price and quality. A price reduction which is gained by reducing quality is not really a price reduction at all, and the public reacts in no uncertain way. There is no quicker or surer way of destroying confidence in a business than to make a price reduction which represents the giving of less and not of more value than before.

However, the reducing of prices solely to increase sales is not a sound business policy, for then the attention may shift from manufacturing to selling. Sales are primarily the result of good manufacturing and not of persuading people to buy. There is no difference between decreasing prices in order to gain sales and maintaining prices just because people seem willing to pay them. If prices are used as baits for buyers, to be raised or lowered as the buyers feel about it, it is in effect a handing over of the control of the business to the buyers to do with as they like. That is a very real control and it is exercised in very drastic fashion. This country has seen it exercised time and again.

The policy of constantly reducing prices has really more to do with management than with sales and should be considered from the manufacturing point of view and not with primary regard to the ideas of the sales end of the business.

If a price be maintained merely because there is apparently no sales reason for reducing it, what is the effect on the management? Does it constantly press to reduce costs so that the maintained price would translate into a

B

***

constantly enlarging profit account? That is exactly what does not happen. The maintenance of the price eventually puts the management to sleep. There is a tendency to let well enough alone, and well enough never can be left alone. Nothing can remain static. Things are either moving forward or moving backward. If a management lets well enough alone for six months or a year, the business will inevitably get out of its control—little items of waste will creep in, bigger items will follow them, and in the end costs will be so high that the profits will vanish. There is no way of keeping a management always at its work unless the economies which it effects are carried over into lower prices and higher wages. For then each advance is marked by a lower price peg. Once a peg is put in, the management must continue to do at least as well as it has ever done. Usually it must do much better. That is why there is more than sales to be considered in a price-lowering policy.

The policy strikes at the very heart of management. If one keeps the price always as high as one can, there is no margin for an increase when fair treatment of the product and the public requires an increased price. The public will meet an increase in a product that has dealt squarely with it before. But it is only when one lowers prices without regard to whether or not the public is willing to pay a higher price that the public maintains a confidence which not only results in steady buying but which permits an advance in prices if conditions should make such an advance necessary. One cannot use a margin and also have it. The public will know from experience that the advance is being made only because it cannot be helped, and therefore it will not resent the advance and no good will will be lost. It is better to have a good margin for a necessary increase than for an enforced drop. A product that has been priced at what the traffic will bear cannot get help from the public in an emergency, and it often cannot get help in itself, because such a policy softens the muscles of management—it has had too much easy living. Thus the pressing for better methods has always with us brought so many unlooked for economies that profits simply cannot be avoided. Our problem has always been to keep profits down and not up. There can be no other result from the price-decreasing policy and the constant challenge to management which it involves.

These fundamentals are not peculiar to the automobile industry and they apply to any business, large or small. They are universal. If they were adopted, a flood of properly made goods would flow through every nook and cranny of the country, drive out high prices, produce employment everywhere at good wages, and make poverty impossible. The getting of these goods into consumption is the problem of business leadership.

The question is not simply to have people buy more goods but to have them buy more of the goods which will benefit them. We use the word "buy" because that is the only method that we know of distributing goods. We must use money.

The limits of production will be reached when everyone has all the goods he needs or can use to increase his comfort in living. And since every improvement in goods or the methods of making creates a new need, the day when we can actually have overproduction is far distant.

Take our theories of what is extravagance and what is economy. In the business world it is considered wasteful for a manufacturer to retain a machine that will satisfactorily do work, if another machine appears which will do the work better or more cheaply. American industry never hesitates to scrap a machine the moment that a better one can be had. That is considered as economy in business. But our old notions of economy, which in business we have shaken off, still hold in the home affairs of the individual. It is considered economical to retain a thing in the home until it is worn out—regardless of the wear and tear that it may involve on the human beings concerned. That is not economy at all but extravagance. We progress as we conserve human energy—as we get more for the expenditure of the same effort. That principle in a true national economy has to be carried over into the life of the home. Our homes and our ways of living are still too much influenced by the Old World standards.

In our younger days we knew men who wore their coats until they were green and threadbare and these men were called thrifty. It was a thrift that hindered progress. There was no exchange, no circulation of services, no life in such an attitude. Goods are made to be used. There can be no other reason for their existence. Use is the power that keeps the wheels of life moving.

But how are the people going to find the money to buy these goods? That again is the business of management—of leadership. If we wait upon demand, we shall wait forever. Demand does not create, it is created. If we begin a large production of goods and make the wages high enough, then a supply of buying power will be spread through the country which will absorb the goods—provided they are properly made and properly priced. And the flow of exchange, which is the blood of society, will be resumed. There is only one way—and the way of production is the beginning of it.

If we should achieve what is called a stabilization of industry, making just what is asked for and no more, the power to buy the goods would fall off—for enough purchasing power to buy would not be distributed. The ideal of stabilization is a pretty one, but it stabilizes the wrong kind of condition. It stabilizes the kind of condition the country wants to be rid of. It would result in certain stagnation, for there would be no pressure towards bettering goods or methods and we should begin to sag.

The purpose of industry is to produce goods that serve people. It is no part of the purpose of industry to support people, and if we start into industry from the angle of making it support a certain number of wage earners, then we destroy the purpose of industry and therefore make it incapable of supporting people. In other words, production exists to create goods which will serve people.

If, however, high wages are not paid and there is no pressure towards ever higher wages as production increases, then the output will not be absorbed and there will be no reason for producing it. Thus, although industry does not primarily exist to pay high wages, it cannot exist in any large serving capacity unless it does pay high wages.

The approach, however, is important. If we imagine that industry exists to support people, then the more men that it employs the better. In this view an employer

who took on two hundred men at two dollars a day would
be better serving the public than one who took on fifty
men at eight dollars a day. That sort of program is often
urged as in the interests of society: employ more men,
they say, even if you have to pay them smaller wages.

It is, on the contrary, directly against the true interests of society and makes for poverty. The man at two
dollars a day will have no surplus spending power at all
and he will not be a factor in the market. The man at
eight dollars a day will have a spending power and in the
use of that power he will be bound to create work so that
the other men will eventually have well-paid employment.
There can be no greater fallacy than thinking that employing large numbers of low-priced men is humane or
helps the country. It is only helping to make poverty
universal by paying low wages and keeping men on, regardless of the demands of the highest production.

The task of industrial leadership is not to find jobs for
as many men as possible but to find high-priced jobs for
as many men as possible, and the start has to be with a
few high-priced men. For not otherwise can the low costs
be attained which will increase consumption and make
more high-priced jobs necessary. Production calls out
man power; production is not called out by man power.

We are travelling a road that no one has ever travelled.
The way is not easy. Many well-meaning people have
held out that there is another road and the going is much
easier. They point to the road of regulated prices, state
aid, and the sanctifying of things as they are. They do
not know that the end of that road is a very hard one.

There can be no substitute—either temporarily or permanently—for work and leadership.

It may be that the road we are on is not worth travelling. But that point should be decided before we take the other road. For we know that the other road leads back to universal poverty.

CHAPTER II

The Fear of Overproduction

ALTHOUGH there is much talk of the dangers of overproduction, the fear is not that the supply of goods will be too great. The real fear is that the supply of profits and wages may be disturbed.

The workman fears that if more is produced than the public will buy he will be unemployed until the public catches up with the oversupply. The employer fears that unsold goods will stagnate and that he may have to sell them at a loss. We are all of us both buyers and sellers. When we are buyers we do not worry lest well-made goods be offered to us too cheaply. We are glad to find the bargains. First-class goods and commodities can always be sold—at a price. It would seem that overproduction is not quite what it pretends to be—it is not a curse to everyone.

It may be possible to have an actual overproduction—a condition in which first-class goods are not bought because everyone already has a supply of them. But it is always a relative condition and not at all to be confused with oversupply. Overproduction is always with reference to a ready market but oversupply is to be considered with reference to the ability of the people to consume the product if they had the money to buy. That is, we think of overproduction when selling becomes slow, whereas only complete fulfillment of need could make us think of oversupply. The condition of oversupply has not as yet obtained in this country. Of what commodity has every citizen yet had enough? What has been called over-production is thus not overproduction at all. The country has had stocks of unsold goods when the power to buy them has been absent. But both the need and the desire to buy are always present. I am assuming, of course, that the unsold goods are of a design and a quality to meet the needs and the desires of the people.

At all times, but especially at the end of a boom, the market contains goods that remain unsold not because of overproduction but because there exists no reason why anyone should buy them—whatever their past usefulness, they no longer fill a need. Their owners may make a great noise about business being bad, but the fact is that the goods are so badly designed and produced as to make it poorer business to sell them than to junk them. Business sometimes seems slow only because the public sense of values and design is moving faster than the inventive re-sources of some manufacturers. In a very real sense it is the personnel of business that is slow and not the public. Most manufacturers know that, all other considerations aside, it does not pay to put out poor stuff. It may be sold for a while, but at some point—the point where public knowledge and taste take a step ahead—the buying will stop and the manufacturer will have on hand unsalable goods. If the channels of business were never clogged with goods that have no excuse for being, a recurrent cause of business depression would be removed.

If, however, first-class goods that do meet needs cannot

be sold in ever-increasing quantities, then the trouble narrows down to an insufficiency of buying power. This may be due to the price of the article being too high or—more commonly—to the price of too many articles being too high. It may not be possible for the manufacturer greatly to lower his prices at that moment, although if he be progressive he will always be able to make some price reductions, but if the public is to be given all possible benefit, the business of price reductions must begin with the price of materials, continue through the cost of manufacture, and be completed in decreased costs of distribution. The manufacturer often sees how swiftly the economies in manufacturing are swallowed up in wasteful distribution and this distribution may not be within the control of the manufacturer. There is no point in economizing in manufacturing if at the same time the suppliers and distributors charge all that the traffic will bear. This is merely to emphasize the fact that the task of putting business on better foundations depends on every department of business and not alone on the manufacturer. Nothing can be cheap when any part of a commodity is dear. The only point where we cannot consider cheapness in the sense of price reductions is in human labor. Labor costs must be kept down but the only infallible way of doing this is by keeping wages up.

In general it can be laid down as a principle that prices to the consumer can always be cut, and in an emergency it may pay to cut the prices to below the line of profit. The increased business will in the course of time create larger profits. We have a number of times cut our prices below what we believed to be the cost of production, and

the immediate benefits have been of two kinds. The larger
volume of business resulting has not been the most valuable of the benefits. That which has most profited us
has been the effect which this arbitrary cutting of costs
has had on our organization—that is, on all of us. It has
always made us more alert and more resourceful. I find
it is more profitable to give more attention to the producing organization than to the selling market. We pay
comparatively little attention to what is called "the sales
end of the business." We believe that the sales are largely
determined by the ability and progressiveness of the manufacturing organization. Therefore it is not without experience that I say prices can always be cut, and with
great benefit to both maker and user.

The lowering of prices may sometimes of itself be
enough to bring articles within the range of buying power.
But buying power is not a constant figure. Lowering
prices is only one way of increasing it. It must be increased absolutely as well as relatively, else the market for
things will not be constantly expanding. Therefore it is
not enough only to lower prices. Industry must also aim
at continuously providing out of its operations a larger
and larger income for everyone connected with it. This
brings up for review in a very fundamental manner the
whole subject of industrial management and finance.

It must be settled in our minds, first, that this thing
which is generally spoken of as overproduction has never
as yet actually occurred. The occasional stagnations in the
free flow of goods from producers to consumers seem to
have no connection whatsoever with the quantity of goods
produced. Instead of fearing genuine overproduction we

should welcome the day when it may be possible, for then everyone will be supplied with all of the goods and services he needs or wants. From the beginning of time there has been a striving for goods. There has never been a period when people in general did not want more and more goods—although there have been periods when people definitely gave up the hope ever of getting them and accepted poverty as an inevitable fact. Some of them were even persuaded that poverty was a virtue instead of a social disease. We must candidly agree with the moralists who contend that mankind does not exist only to possess material objects, but it is most certainly true that, until society from top to bottom is satiated with goods, we shall scarcely have the opportunity really to discover what life is about. Therefore we can look forward to the day of actual overproduction as the day of emancipation from enslaving materialistic anxiety. Unfortunately there is no prospect of that day coming soon. The people as a whole have not as yet suffered from plenty.

Of the three elements which alone or in combination cause the stagnation which is so wrongly spoken of as overproduction, two are within the control of business itself, while the third is largely within its control. Quality and price are affairs of design, engineering, and management while the increasing of buying power is, for that portion of the nation's income which results from industry, an affair of design, engineering, management, and finance.

Since a surplus of unsold goods is never due to factories having actually produced too much, it is not surprising that the superficial view that depressions are due to overproduction invariably leads to adopting measures to relieve the situation, which in fact only makes conditions worse. The patient is given a drastic treatment for a disease he has not.

In the older days of medicine the doctor, after making his diagnosis, invariably let out some of the patient's life blood. The patient was supposed to get stronger by being made weaker. Our business doctoring is still in that stage.

The prescriptions, whatever they pretend to be, all get around to raising prices, cutting down production, and decreasing the buying power of wages both directly and indirectly. A very fashionable prescription aims at cutting down the production until it exactly fits the demand. It is an interesting thought but it proceeds upon the fallacy that production depends upon demand. The opposite is the truth for business. Demand depends upon production and so if the production drops the demand will drop and therefore under this proposed scheme production and demand will go hand in hand to oblivion. This, however, is not very serious, for an industry that would consent to have the amount of its business fixed by rule is headed for oblivion anyway. Many territorial arrangements between sections of an industry fall under the same head. Sometimes these arrangements are disguised as mergers. A merger of corporations may be distinctly beneficial in bringing together a number of units that belong together, but it is more usual for weak than for strong corporations to merge. No lamp posts have been provided for weak or overstimulated business to cling to and so they are apt to cling to one another. The embrace is called a merger.

However, the reorganizing of so many industries to meet the conditions of to-day—even though the reorganizations do not meet the conditions—is at least a recognition that the need for reorganizing exists and that we have passed the peak of a certain phase of industry. The recognition of that fact is the first step toward a more thorough reorganization which will insure steady progression and make impossible the recurrence of such orgies as have from time to time taken place in the stock market.

The changes which are now coming about are, as has been indicated, very comprehensive. They involve more of a change in our mental attitude toward things than in the things themselves. We need a new view of the business unit, of its profits, of employment, and of thrift. Essentially we must get rid of the notion that we are the servants of business and proceed to put business in its proper place as our servant. This means that all along the line we shall have to cease serving things and make things serve us. We need a higher and more wholesome thrift in which things will be valued only for the service they render and only so long as they render it. We have to get rid of that miserly attitude which is born of fear and which results in hoarding instead of using. This applies to our business organization as well as to our personal affairs. A change has already come about and we might as well realize it. The change need not of itself bother anyone. It is the natural order. The pessimist who sees things going to pieces is not deluded; he is correctly reporting what he actually sees. The optimist who sees things soaring to perfection is an equally good reporter—he sees what he says he sees. But neither sees the whole picture.

Their reports of what they see are true, but they are not comprehensive. Certain established customs, methods, processes, institutions, and traditions are undoubtedly going to pieces, and irrecoverably. This irrecoverability strikes fear in many people. They want yesterday to come back. But yesterday is not coming back. The old era is dead and is being buried bit by bit.

It is the collapse of many dominant methods and institutions that alarms people. That need not alarm anyone. The evolution is perfectly natural.

One of the great changes that have come about has to do with the increasingly large number of men who are no longer working exclusively for money. To-day none of the real leaders is working for money. All of them have more money than they can use, and they continue to earn money in large amounts as a part of the machinery of monetary supply for the whole of society. All so-called private fortunes are nothing less than public reserves. I have noticed that those who work exclusively for money and for a time earn it do not retain it unless they continue the use of it for the public. The desire for mere money has a way of defeating itself—a very sure way. It is quite the same with a business and particularly so under the new order of things. If the main objective of any business is the earning of a fixed dividend, then that business is surely doomed. Profits must come as an incident to doing the job well or they will not come at all. There is nothing fixed about any business and it has to be prepared at any time to change its product and methods of manufacturing. A unit of industry, a business—call it anything—is only slightly a collection of buildings and machinery. An estimate of the value of any business based on the property or facilities it owns is practically worthless. No one would think of paying carpenters according to the kind of tool chests they had. The man with a good set of tools ought to do better work than the man with a poor set and therefore command a higher wage. But that would have to be demonstrated; it could not be taken for granted.

A factory is only a tool, and its value lies in its production. This production is based on the power and the methods that the managers have put behind it. In many respects the factory itself is a greater thing than its product. If the product is a machine of any sort useful to the public, that is the thing admired; but the really admirable object is the machine that makes the machine: the factory organization and equipment that make the thing which the public buys. The factory is a potency which may be turned to many uses besides that for which the public knows it best. Power, the knowledge of power, the use of power, and not merely the specific product of power in which for the moment we happen to be interested—that is what an industrial establishment signifies.

A manufacturing company is only as good as its product, and unless that product be constantly improved it will not constantly draw the public to its buying. That is elementary, but often this fundamental seems to be neglected, for not otherwise could so many companies be judged for financial purposes solely on their past records. A record of success presupposes that some valuable experience has been gained. But if the company loses its active management—the men who made its success—then that company, no matter how much property it has, must make its way all over again unless the new managers are able to avail themselves of the former experience. This is frequently shown in an old company which under a new management goes in for quantity production, not to meet demands as they are created, but just to produce a great quantity of goods to force on the market. Under these circumstances quality is always neglected. The neglect may not be—probably is not—intentional, but if the emphasis of the management is upon volume then the men all the way down the line will feel it, inspection will be put aside if it interferes with output records, and of course the quality will go down.

The only things of any great intrinsic value in our group of industries, for instance, are the materials and supplies of a general nature which are on hand awaiting fabrication to our special ends, and these we keep down to a minimum. As for the buildings and machinery, they must be valued in dollars according to the meaningless methods of accounting that are required by law. Actually they are worth only what we can do with them. Our shop is not the mere material fabric: it is twenty-five years of time, twenty-five years of experience, built into management and method and machinery. The greatest elements of a machine or a shop are those you do not see —the invisible essence of time and devotion and slowly acquired wisdom that has gone into it. It is our business as managers to design a shop that will make the product, and, since every day we should learn something about how to better our product or the manner of its making, both the product and the shop are constantly changing.

Our policy—which we have found no reason to amend —has been to regard ourselves as charged with discovering the best way of doing everything and to hold every process employed in our manufacturing as purely experimental. Several years ago I said:

"We know from the changes that have already been brought about that far greater changes are to come, and that therefore we are not performing a single operation as well as it ought to be performed. We do not make changes for the sake of making them, but we never fail to make a change once it is demonstrated that the new way is better than the old way. We hold it our duty to permit nothing to stand in the way of progress—in the way of giving better service with all that follows in wages and prices."

This policy keeps one continuously balancing the merits of improvements both in methods of making and in design. This, of course, includes materials, for in no direction has there been greater progress than in the working out of new and stronger steels and composite metals. Some changes are forced by the shortage of materials, and some by the unreasonably high prices imposed by the material suppliers, but the majority are the results of experience. The first question to answer concerning any suggested change is:

Will it result in better service? Service runs in many directions. Among them may be listed:

(1) Lower costs. This is a service to wages, profits, and prices, and thus to more business.

(2) Strength and durability. These serve everyone.

(3) Appearance. This is a factor of rising importance.

After examining a suggestion from the end of service, one has then to go into the cost of making the change as compared with the economy to be effected. One has to take the long view and estimate in the light of experience whether the change will increase volume.

It has been our policy since 1908 to have a single base model with a few variations based on accommodation to various needs, and make improvements on that model from time to time, but without abandoning the fundamental conception of the model. That was our contribution toward checking obsolescence in the hands of the owner.

The trouble with mass production—and the phrase "mass production" is quite misleading—is that it tends to become rigid and keeps on producing regardless of the market. It has been supposed that our company was an exponent of mass production. That has never been true, and I have often explained why it was not true. We have merely made a great many automobiles using the methods which we found most economical. The product has always ruled the methods of making. This is another way of saying that the needs of the public have ruled.

Rigid machine production of the kind known as mass production quickly comes to an end, for it violates the first principle of large-scale production—which is that the makers must constantly improve the design and quality of the goods turned out. That is the inexorable law of production and it has been proved time and again. Only a few of the standard articles of twenty years ago are the standard articles of to-day. Why? Those earlier articles became standard only because they always met the needs of the people. They were bought because they could always be depended upon to be first-class, but they were first-class only because they were constantly improved—although possibly the improvements were seldom mentioned. But if, after the reputation of the articles had become assured, and those who had built the reputation rested, or were followed by men who were content to take the product as they found it and depend on the fine reputation, then dry rot set in and the product steadily slipped back and another product took its place. No product ever remains standard. It has to be kept standard.

It is true that mass production frequently piles up great stocks of goods which cannot be sold and this leads to the belief that mass production results in overproduction. Inflexible mass production does start to pile up goods the moment the goods cease to suit the buyer or are too high in price, but this is not the fault of the production methods. It is the fault of the managers in thinking that one design or one method can for long continue. Indeed, if mass production were what it is supposed to be, there would be some cause for alarm—but only among the mass producers. For they would lose by it. It is the large producers who constantly change methods and designs; it is the small producers who cannot change. Among the peasants of Europe or the coolies of the Far East life is standardized. For endless generations they have been doing the same things the same way. Machine production in this country has diversified our life, has given a wider choice of articles than was ever before thought possible—and also it has provided the means wherewith the people may buy them. We standardize only on essential conveniences.

Standardization, instead of making for sameness, has introduced unheard-of variety into our life. It is surprising that this has not been generally perceived.

All of this involves quite a fundamental change in corporate finance. A company must do more than keep its plant and equipment in repair. It must continually be changing them to meet changes in design, materials, and methods of making—not a single item of equipment can be regarded as permanent. Not even the site can be taken as fixed. We abandoned our Highland Park plant—which was in its day the largest automobile plant in the world—and moved to the River Rouge plant because in the new plant there could be less handling of materials and consequently a saving. We frequently scrap whole divisions of our business—and as a routine affair. And then one has to be prepared against the day when a complete change may be necessary and an entirely new plant constructed to make a new product. We have gone through all of this.

In these days a plant, no matter how much it costs, is worth only its value as scrap metal, for a complete change in methods may require, almost any day, that it be reduced to scrap. Hence a business is not really solvent unless it has a reserve in money which will permit it to make any needed changes at once and out of its own money. A business is financially unsafe if it has to borrow money to meet the needs of progress. For it cannot pay off the loan out of profits and at the same time provide a new reserve against more changes in the future without charging more for its product than it should charge. It cannot, if necessary, go for a time on the no-profit basis just to step up trade. A reserve in money is just as necessary as are the tools of production, but at the same time a business is under the obligation of paying out as much as possible of the money that it receives or else it will not distribute a sufficient purchasing power to make possible the buying of its product. That is an important part of the process of keeping up a constantly increasing flow of goods.

The maintaining of too large a reserve tends to withdraw too much purchasing power from the public, while maintaining too small a reserve endangers the continuance of the business. In our case we for years maintained a large reserve because we knew that some day we should have to make sweeping changes.

Now that we have made one complete change and know about what it cost, we have decided to keep a sufficient cash balance on hand and then endeavour so to fix our prices and our wages that our income and outgo will balance. This does not mean that our business will be managed as a kind of charity—it would not last long as a charity. No one will be paid for other than work. But what is the point of taking profits if one does not want them? The wages of the workmen are more important to the country than the dividends to stockholders. There is nothing at all to do with profits except to put them back into industry, and this is true whether or not the profits stay in the company as surplus or are distributed as wages or dividends. The business of maintaining life is the only proper use of money.

What has this to do with overproduction? Everything. For that which is called overproduction comes about in

part from unreasoned production and in part from not
paying attention to the building of buying power. And
no attention can be given either to reasoning production
in terms of needs or to building buying power, unless
the finances of the corporation are handled in a broad industrial way instead of in a narrow financial way.

CHAPTER III

LABOUR SERVING OR LABOUR SAVING?

IF A machine be regarded only as a way of saving labour—as a method by which an employer can do with fewer men—then it may be a hardship to everyone. The workers who broke up the first power loom were logical according to their lights; in fact the whole opposition to the introduction of power and machinery has had a reasonable foundation. The rebellion—although few know it—is against the use of machinery as a mere substitute for hand labour. The phrase "labour saving" is current as evidence of how little the function of machinery is understood. For unless machinery is *labour serving* it has no excuse for being.

The proper and profitable use of machinery for production demands a very different conception of the industrial organization from that which was held in the old hand days—or in the days when machines were only aids to man power. That was, properly, the machine age. But now, as a matter of fact, the machine age has passed. We are now in the process of finding out how best to make machines serve us. They are now just a part in a new order.

This does not seem wholly to be grasped. Much of to-day's thinking is still in the stage of fitting labour-serving machines into a hand-labour kind of society. They cannot be so fitted and much that is blamed on machines should be blamed on a lack of comprehension of the new life that we are in. We fail to realize that if we are to have things continuously in more abundance we cannot also preserve all of the traditions of the old isolated, self-contained society. Neither can we preserve the old dependent relation between the employee and the employer. The world does not owe any of us a living, but we all owe livings to one another.

It seems that the time when people begin to get excited over an industrial movement is also just about the time when the movement is either waning or has considerably changed its form. When the prophets get together and decide when and how disaster is coming, the conditions from which they predict disaster have already changed. It has always been so with machinery. Every little while someone, without a complete knowledge of the subject, gets a general notion of what is going on and then starts in to predict and to forecast. The note of their prophecies is that the world will soon be so full of machines as to leave no place for men.

Some machinery does displace men, but that is only a stage in its development. A ditch may be more effectively dug by a power shovel than by a gang of men, but that is a displacement in the interests of humanity, for merely moving earth around with a shovel is not a human sort of a job. Cheapening the digging of ditches allows more ditches to be dug and among the many consequences of cheap ditches are better drainage and health, a demand for pipe, the removal of ugly and dangerous wires, and so on and on. It soon works out that the ditching machine, while a blessing to everyone, is a most particular blessing to the man who once dug ditches, for it opens up new and better work for him.

Machinery driven by power is only a tool, and if we consider even the highest developments of machinery only as tools, the situation becomes somewhat easier to comprehend. A foot rule is a tool, but it does not save labour in the sense of destroying jobs. Without the element of measurement we could not have industry. A chisel does not save labour; it enables a man to do what he could not otherwise do. One first-class carpenter can put up more and better buildings than a thousand cavemen. He does not displace a thousand men; he just does what they, without tools, could not do. If the carpenter must cut down the trees to make boards with his set of tools, he can do far less than if the boards are delivered to him. If the lumbering and mill work has been done by machinery, then the boards will come to him finished, and on them he need use only his skill instead of both his skill and his muscle. The machinery has served him. No one in this country regrets the passing of the chimney sweep. Yet chimney sweeping was once the livelihood of many persons.

No one can deny that a workman needs tools of some sort with which to work. But is there a point at which the fineness of the tools causes less work instead of more work? It is not necessary to discuss the point as to whether industry exists to provide work for men or to provide goods for men. There happens to be no conflict between providing goods and providing work, just as there is no conflict between low costs and high wages. If machinery, no matter how simple or how complex, be used for any purpose other than providing a free flow of goods at the lowest possible prices, then the balance between production and consumption is hurt and there will be few jobs for men. But also there will be few buyers for the products of the machines, and the machines will be only liabilities to their owners. If a machine be regarded as labour saving instead of as labour serving, it may become a menace. The fault is not, however, in the machine but in the managers of it.

There is no point at which the development of the machine is a menace. An iron chisel is better than a flint one, and a steel chisel is better than an iron one. Could there be a point where the cutting quality of the chisel could be made so fine that it would be a menace? Obviously not.

There is a great deal of wrong in the theory. It is founded not on fact but on very superficial reasoning. A good deal of the reasoning starts with the error of assuming that machinery is merely "labour saving" because someone in the past called it "labour saving." Most of our more important machines to-day do not save labour except in a larger sense. They either do things which could not be done by hand, or which would not be done at all, had not the machines come in to make the product cheap enough to touch a universal demand.

The automobile is only one of hundreds of commodities that have been made possible by the machine. One may look at the automobile as only an extension of the power of man, but it is really a thing of itself. A man may go faster on roller skates than he can on foot, and on a bicycle he can make his strength still more efficient. But in an automobile he contributes only guidance and control. His personal strength is not of moment. The automobile is really, therefore, not a labour-saving device at all. It enables the doing of things that would not otherwise be done. A drop-forging machine is in a way doing what men might do with heavy hammers, but an upsetting machine—which presses a bit of metal into shape—is doing something requiring a strength and power not attainable by human beings. Up until 1925 our factories had never used as much as thirty million kilowatt hours of electrical power in a month. It was not until last year that we ever touched forty million a month, but now we are around sixty million. To think of such amounts of power in terms of slaves, or of substituting for the strength of men, or in any human terms is only distorting the picture, for human strength could not possibly be mobilized to exert any such amount of power in one place.

The power is nothing of itself. It has to be used through machines. It cannot be used through men. These machines are therefore more than mere extensions of the human hands. They are labour serving—not labour saving. Describing them in terms of labour saved brings in the thought that there is only so much work to be done in the world, and that there is a choice between doing it with men and doing it with machines. There is no such choice. The work simply could not be done by men.

It is quite generally believed that the introduction of machinery to do work formerly done by men creates unemployment. That, however, is not usually the case, for if the machines are properly used they will create more employment than before, and the period of change will be neither long nor difficult. The larger unemployment arises from the wiping out of whole industries through technical progress, or in those industries or sections of industries that refuse to keep up with the advances in science or in practice. We can never have any prolonged unemployment if the leaders in industry stay fully awake. Only such industries as oversleep awaken to find themselves not needed. And we are always better off for the ending of sleepy industries, for they invariably are low-wage industries.

It used to be taken for granted that quantity production had to be rough-and-ready. It was thought that the machine was not as accurate as the skilled worker. When I first went into the large-scale production of automobiles, a tolerance of one hundredth of an inch was in the region of extreme accuracy. But the public, especially in automobiles, has become educated to demand better workmanship, so that now a tolerance of one thousandth of an inch is common and a tolerance of one ten thousandth is not uncommon. Such accuracy would be out of the question in other than the most expensive, skilled hand work. The older machinery and methods of production would not give this accuracy.

It cannot be too often repeated that production and design must go together. The tools have not yet been devised that will make any part exactly to a measurement. The nearest approach to absolute exactness is in our Johanssen gauge department, which controls the gauges throughout all our industries. On the blue print the exact measurement of a part is put down. This exact size is not always attained, and so in addition to the measurement there is noted what is called the "permitted tolerance"—which means that the part may be a certain fraction of an inch above or below the designated size.

When we began quantity manufacturing, years ago, the tolerances were rather large, although smaller than on any piece of machinery that had previously been made in quantity. This had to be because there were no machines in existence which could produce more precise work. As the years passed and we developed better machinery the tolerances grew much closer, until when we retooled our industries we were able to take a big jump in precision. We made a limit of three ten thousandths of an inch rather common, while on a few parts we put the limit at one ten thousandth. This precision is not demanded simply as a test of skill. The better fitted the parts of a machine, the better work it will do, and the longer it will last. The motor of our present product is only slightly larger and slightly heavier than the old motor, but it gives double the power. It could not have been designed to do this had we not undertaken to bring about a new order of precision in quantity manufacturing. The fact here to be noted is that it has fundamentally changed the function of machines and the character of the men who work with them. A thousandth of an inch has proved to have large consequences in the employment of men.

These consequences run exactly counter to the ordinary ideas on the subject. With crude machinery the man must be a part of the machine and function with it, and under these circumstances he is at his best when restricted to a single operation. We carried that principle farther than

ever it had been carried—so far indeed as to show us it
was only a step on the way. Workmen have very generally suspected or resisted scientific management and in
this they have been more instinctively right than most
managers are willing to acknowledge. It is right for a
man to resist being made into a machine. We regulated
the speed of the men by the speed of the conveyor and
found it possible to get a large and economical production
at a moderate, steady pace and to reflect it in our wage
rates and in our selling prices. No manufacturing economy is worth while unless it be translated into both wages
and sales prices. It does not do to put all of the savings
into the sales prices, for then the wage earners are not
added to the list of possible customers. And putting all of
the savings into profits is very short-sighted, for the profits
go to comparatively few people and have very little effect
upon consumption.

We began first to eliminate hard work, and then we discovered that machines could be devised to take the place
of many hand operations or operations where the machine
had wholly to be controlled by hand. This quickly led
us to machines that did more than one operation, as, for
instance, boring a number of holes at once, or performing
several operations on a part at the same time, or even,
with automatic or quasi-automatic machines, completing
a whole part. A full automatic machine is one that requires no human attention; a quasi-automatic requires an
attendant—if only to put in the unfinished part and take
out the finished one. And thus we began to learn that the
minute subdivision of labour was based on man power
and neglected the possibilities of machine power. Then

we started to find machines that would do many operations at the same time and we began to group operations
instead of separating them as before. This is the road to
automatic machinery.

The present problem is to discover the principles and
work out the designs for automatic machinery that will
completely turn out articles of whatever accuracy of
measurement may be required. We have one job right
now that needs great accuracy and which employs nine
hundred men. That whole job could be far better done
by the right kind of machine with very few attendants.
Such a machine will have to be devised. Accurate, large-
scale production must now have automatic or nearly automatic machines in order to reduce the cost and the errors
of human labour. And so many of these machines will
shortly be required that the making of them will come out
of the specialty and fall into the high-production class.

Machinery is thus developing rapidly to take the
position of the old craftsman in production. This is an
advantage, for it both raises the quantity of production
and increases the possible earnings of men. If a man
works with a machine which will produce one hundred
units as against one by hand, then more people can have
goods and at the same time the man is demonstrating a
higher earning power. The man who helps make the
machine which in turn makes the machine which actually
produces goods is in a position to be paid more highly
than the most skilled man in the production of goods—
for he furnishes the means for high production. And
while the machine itself may have only a single purpose,
the mechanics who make the machines or who manage

them must be in the nature of all-around men. This is one of the machine developments which have not been foreseen.

The actual development runs exactly counter to tradition and it is going to take some years to train men to view themselves as general mechanics and artisans capable of quickly learning to manage almost any kind of machine. There will always be places for expert hand craftsmen, as they are artists and are to be regarded as such. But they will not be used in production, for there is no use in wasting the time of an artist doing tasks which a machine can do quite as well and usually better.

The spirit of craftsmanship may be in everyone, but the ability to become a real craftsman is reserved for the very few, and these few will come to the top under any circumstances. The usual average man will learn just so much and no more about any job that he is put at, and there is no point in pretending that he is a mentally hungry human being with a gnawing appetite for knowledge. Possibly he ought to be and possibly he will be all that, but he never has been and is not to-day. The run of journeymen mechanics, or artisans, have only a certain skill that they bring to their tasks, and only the most exceptional man can meet an unusual situation. They must be both led and supervised in order to do first-class work.

The tendency in the crafts, therefore, is on one side toward greater specialization and on the other toward greater freedom. In carpentry, for example, the special parts of buildings which were formerly made by the carpenter on the job are now put together by special machinery in the factory and only set in place by the carpenter on the job. This release from special requirements brings the opportunity or the necessity to widen the individual's field of work, so that now we find a generation of men who know how to be helpful along many lines, who in fact have a very moderate amount of knowledge of half-a-dozen jobs instead of a knowledge of only one job. The old jibe about "a jack-of-all-trades" is out of fashion. No knowledge now comes amiss to a man in doing his work. So many formerly unrelated lines of work now enter into the production of the simplest article that a man must be made versatile in spite of himself. We have discovered that while a man may never attain the status of a specialist on any job, which few ever attained even under the old system, he can attain a moderate mastery of half-a-dozen different kinds of jobs as easily as of one. An ability to work at a wide variety of tasks with an understanding of what he is doing is a necessary characteristic of the new kind of general workman that modern industry needs. Such workmen are developing rather rapidly, but in changing over our industries we could have used many more of them had they been available.

This is a world of change. No industry ever stands still, and no industrial unit ever stands still. Every company in this country is either going forward or going back—according to the necessity for the service which it performs and the quality of its performance. It is very comforting to think of a great manufacturing company as an institution which will go on forever and be a source of livelihood to a large body of people. That simply cannot be, but fortunately, as one industry passes out, another greater and more important industry always takes its place.

Neither the factory nor the job can be regarded as permanent. Both are transient. The view of a job as a fixed income producer will need revision. There can be no such fixity. An industry will exist only so long as it is useful. Beyond that point it should not exist.

CHAPTER IV

THE PLACE OF WAGES

THE paying and the receiving of wages involve a great deal more than the mere transferring of a sum of money. The whole paying of wages as well as the hiring out for a wage has been clouded by tradition. There is, on the one hand, the master-and-servant tradition in which the master is supposed to be kind and appreciative and the servant to be dependent and grateful. On the other hand is the big-family conception in which equality, harmony, and democracy of management figure.

In my view of wages and the relation of the employer and the employee, they are not a small universe in themselves; both are part of and dependent on the larger social world. The amount of work done for society and the amount of money society may profitably pay for that work determine the industrial relation, although that in turn is determined by the quality and extent of the service which industry may render. Improvement in these relations is always possible where the will to improvement exists.

But it is necessary to get away entirely from the thought that the relation between employers and employees has in it anything of meniality. Employers and employees are to be judged by the same standard—are they efficient or are they inefficient? An employer who is not fit for his job comes under the same law as any other inefficient worker. There is nothing in his status as employer that will save him. He has responsibilities but no divine right. If he is a good man in his job he will pay good wages, just as he will make a good product. And his workmen, directed by him, will be enabled to earn good wages. It is a matter of efficiency, not philanthropy. The only pride or satisfaction either may have in it, or even gratitude, is the feeling that this is a world that yields right results to right efforts.

But the relation between employer and employee is not in the least a sentimental one, and the artificial cultivation of good feeling only tends to obscure the real objectives. An artfully arranged attempt to stimulate good feeling usually has for its purpose the concealment of some deep source of bad feeling. Good feeling arises from the situation, or not at all. The paying and receiving of money is the paying and receiving of money. If it be not earned, it cannot be paid, and it should not be paid if it could be. If it be earned, then there is no reason for the employee being grateful for being paid what is justly due, nor for the employer being self-righteously proud for paying it. This view of the relation between the employer and the employee has many consequences which flow counter to the accepted tradition.

Yet you will hear the duties of employers and the rights of employees discussed as if their relation were the only one in the world that mattered—as if these two comprehended all society instead of being only a part of it. It is a curious fact that those who most denounce the industrial order are also those who most insistently try to root it into the very heart of society by making the relation between employer and employee the deepest and most embracing relation between men. It cannot be done. We are all part of a larger order.

Look at this in the light of a concrete instance. It is our belief that the shop is not a permanent thing and that it can exist only so long as it serves. The moment that it has ceased serving, good management will scrap it, or else inexorable social disapproval will. If the obstacle to service is not fundamental, then it may not be necessary to scrap the whole shop but merely to reconstruct it. We ourselves, although we regard nothing in our shops or the shops themselves as permanent and everything as continuously changing, reached a point where it was necessary fundamentally to change our product and its method of making. So we scrapped what was then held to be the largest automobile plant in the world, saved and removed what machinery could be used or adapted for use, placed some of it in another plant which at the same time we reconstructed and then distributed the rest of the machinery among plants in this country and throughout the world. The whole tractor plant was sent to Ireland.

This may seem to have nothing to do with wages. It has everything to do with wages, for these changes enabled us better to serve the public and therefore to pay higher wages. While these changes were going on, some of the men who had worked in the departments that were being dismantled were temporarily without jobs, others had to go into jobs very different from what they had been accustomed to, while others could not fit themselves into the new series of jobs that the new set-up brought about. If we had acted under the theorist's conception that the employer's primary duty is to the man employed instead of to the public, we should not have made the changes, with the net result that to-day, instead of having more jobs than ever before and higher wages than ever before, we should have fewer jobs because we should have less business. And we should have a lowering scale of wages instead of a rising, and everyone would be worse off and no one would be better off.

If a company operates on the theory that it owes a living to those who work for it, then in the course of time it will pass out—and be unable to pay the debt it thinks it owes. Exactly the same condition will be brought about by acting on the theory that the stockholders must always have dividends. Unless the primary service be to the public, no one will be served.

This principle does not seem thoroughly to be understood and it is often difficult to apply, for sometimes its application seems harsh. It seems to imply an indifference to human beings. But, in truth, it has human welfare as its motive. The plight of the men who become temporarily unemployed in the process seems much more important to the unthinking observer than the eventually increased service to all. It is difficult to see the whole picture and to realize that the fortunes of any individual or of any group are always best served when they are made part of a larger service. The individual or the group through a short-sighted view of their interests may be wholly blameless of intentionally retarding progress, yet that is the result of any preference of private before public good.

The right of a man to work is a sacred right, but to preserve a job just because it is a job may seem to be kind-
ness to an individual, but it will be at the expense of a
great many others who do not appear in the picture but
who are just as worthy and conscientious as he is. Such
reasoning, however, seems hard, not because there is any
harshness in progress itself, but only because we view
progress against a background of so many fallacies. When
applied to wage earners it seems hard only because of our
traditional conception of master and servant and that
somehow the workman is a menial dependent on his employer. Indeed many worthy people cannot comprehend
any other relation and, during those periods when the
men who should be leading business fail to lead and consequently work is slack, the cry "Give men jobs" arises.
Everyone would recognize the absurdity of employers
parading bearing signs "Give us orders." There is essentially no difference between the actual position of the
employer and the employee. That is the point. If an employer gets his orders through favours and believes that
because he has served certain customers for a long time
this is in itself a reason for having their orders continue,
he is acting on the same false principle as the employee
who thinks that his having held a job establishes upon
his employer the duty of always providing him with a
job. It is a poor rule that will not work for both alike.
Long service by either employer or employee should be
a reason for continued service—for the experience gained
should render their service better than that which anyone
else can give. A worker should have so profited by length
of service as to make himself more valuable than any man

without his experience. The same applies to an employer. But the test of a company, of a workman—or anybody or anything—is solely to be found in the service rendered. And in the end I think that it will be discovered that if all of us—no matter what may at the moment be our respective situations—rid ourselves of the notion that the world or anyone else owes us a living, we shall be the better for it. The approach of dependency, whether in a man or in a corporation, is the approach of helplessness and leads to the asking of a living by favour instead of a living by merit. The corporation which goes out seeking only profits does not get far and neither does the man who goes out seeking only wages—instead of work.

There is no natural level of wages, just as there is no natural level of profits. The conception of a natural level of wages arises out of a state of society in which everything even to the smallest detail is hallowed by tradition. If the inventiveness of an industry comes to a standstill —and this happens whenever an industry gets solely in the control of the financial point of view—then there will be a level of wages and for a time there will be a level of profits. But this level will be only temporary and will steadily be lowered. Industry that has found its level will soon be out of tune with the public—which never finds a level—and will cease to render a service, and then both profits and wages will begin to diminish and finally will reach the vanishing point.

It cannot be too often emphasized that just as there are no essential businesses, also there are no essential industries. If an industry does not serve us we find ourselves involuntarily turning to something else and what

is at first taken as a substitute for the essential turns
out to be better than the essential. Gasoline and rubber
are at present essentials to the automobile industry but,
if either should become very poor in quality or very high in
price over any considerable period, the automobile industry
would find substitutes which would quickly be developed
to a point that would forever bar gasoline and rubber—
no matter how high the quality or how fair the price. I
do not know what those substitutes would be and probably
we shall never have to discover them. I only know that if
we must have them we shall have them.

The talking about a natural and stable level of wages
and profits is a sign of sick business. It is equally a sign
of sick business to talk about *arbitrarily* raising wages.
That is not different from *arbitrarily* raising prices. A
high wage is as destructive as a *high* price. What is felt
to be *high* is out of relation. Right wages are never felt
to be high any more than right prices are felt to be high.
Right wages and right prices leave everyone with a sense
of satisfaction. The best wages are not high so far as
manufacturing costs are concerned. The wages which
bring prosperity are those which develop out of the inventiveness and engineering skill of the management—
combined with the adaptability and coöperation of the
men. If the wage comprehension of the management does
not extend beyond having the men take a low wage and
the wage comprehension of the men does not extend beyond the management paying a high wage, it will be a
case of stalemate and it really does not make much difference what wages are paid, for the industry and all the
jobs in it will soon be at an end.

In all this, our country as a whole is making a great deal of progress toward a better comprehension of the situation. No one can say that the industry of to-day is not producing more comfort and leisure for the world than that of yesterday. Anyone who prefers to break the ice in his water pitcher in the morning rather than take hot water from a tap can do so without being punished by the industrial system. It is a very free system.

The general condition of prosperity is always a subject of disagreement. There are always those who say that it will not last. The prosperity of the country has always gone forward—even while it was very generally being decided that it was going back. Prosperity is not an accident but something to be cultivated. But it would be very unfortunate to have everyone satisfied with his state of being, for then we should be in great danger.

Yet surely we have moved forward. This is proved by the very nature of the current criticism. Once upon a time people asked only for food; now the critics say that our prosperity is harmful because the people's minds are not developing. Never before has the country been well enough fed to inquire into the state of its mind. And also it is encouraging to note that poverty here and there is brought forward as an exhibit of the weakness of our system. Formerly the poor were taken for granted, and there were far too many of them to be used as exhibits. Poverty was then held as a natural state. Now it is thought to be unnatural. And soon we shall treat poverty as a disease. We shall create a social immunity from it. That is progress.

It will not accomplish this desirable end to pay low

wages as a matter of national policy and then to provide
against poverty by public services financed out of taxes.
Such a programme really never reduces poverty. It accepts
poverty as a natural condition and then provides against
destitution. But in the long run this plan will not even
provide against destitution in an industrial state. The low
wages will prevent any expansion of the home market,
for the standard of living will be at the subsistence point.
The low wages will do more harm than that—for they
will make the goods expensive. If an employer can have
as many men as he likes at low wages he will be inclined
to limit his expenditures for machinery and new designs,
for on the low-wage scale they apparently will not pay.
And so he will produce out-of-date goods at high prices.
The home market for these will be limited. He may gain
a foreign market, but this, too, will be limited by price
and so in the end the sources of wages and of taxation
will dry up.

The only effective wage policy is one that presses forward toward higher wages, lower costs, and lower prices,
and in all this we have a long distance still to go, for
everything in this country is much too high—except wages.
They are too low. In the old business system everything
but profits was considered in the light of a necessary evil.
A sales price was nearly always fixed in the hope of selling somebody something for more than it was worth. The
older business man aimed to sell to a rather narrow circle
which he called his trade, and it never occurred to him
that he could sell to a whole nation. Therefore he very
naturally saw his product in the terms of a very few
people and could bargain with those people. Those who

sold him his materials had exactly the same outlook and
bargained with him on prices. And when it came to employing assistants and workmen he followed the same
procedure. If a customer needed his goods, that customer
was jacked up to pay a high price, but if, on the contrary,
the manufacturer needed the money, the customer had
the whip hand. If there were more workmen around than
jobs, wages were low, while, if there were more jobs than
workmen, wages were high. It never occurred to the older
employers—and this is the condition in Europe to-day—
that high wages were anything more than an additional
cost of production.

Wages are a cost of production, but it does not follow
that merely by paying low wages one will achieve low
costs of production. The way to low costs is through the
intelligent provision of power and machinery and the
keeping of the various factors of business in balance. No
employer has the right to ask a man to work with intelligence unless he pays him for that intelligence. Good
workmanship has to be paid for, and good workmanship is cheap at almost any price. It is simply a waste
of time and money to erect an elaborate manufacturing
equipment and then expect that it can be run by low-paid
men.

There is nothing sentimental about wages. Hiring men
because they are cheap will ruin a business as quickly as
buying material just because it is cheap. There is something like a natural law which makes sharing not only
instinctive but also compulsory. It would not be possible,
for instance, to run our business or any other modern
business with slaves—no matter how skilled and intelligent

the slaves were. And this is regardless of the effect that
wage payments have on consumption, for unless the interest—that is to say, the mind—of a man be employed,
there is no use employing just his hands. His wage must
represent something in the nature of a sharing.

There is nothing that any man can do, the benefits of
which he can restrict to himself alone. Society is so constructed that any good produced overflows its original
limits and benefits the adjacent people. The supreme folly
of selfish intention is that it cannot be carried out. The
intention may be present and the selfishness may be unlimited, but natural law frustrates the intended consequences. The surgeon may practise for fame and wealth
alone, but his very fame and wealth depend upon his
giving benefit. The baker may bake in the utmost selfishness, caring only for the money his craft will bring him,
but nevertheless his bread feeds others. Whether we like
it or not, one never produces a benefit for one's self alone.
No fortune was ever accumulated without increasing the
means of wealth to a multitude. Indeed, vast possessions
have always supported more people than if the ownership were divided, for there is a magic in consolidated
management.

Private ownership, considered in the absolute, extends
only a little way. About the only thing a man can own
absolutely privately is his experience. Our theory of the
private ownership of property—that is, the right of every
man to full security in what he has earned—is based on
this privacy of experience. What belongs to a man should
be his own.

The fact is, we live in a world where nothing has value

until it is shared. The value rises in proportion to the number of people who possess it. Creative power does not exist except in company with the desire to share. The very attempt to hide away a value casts doubt on its being a value. Prosperity means to us that the families in the next street, those at the other end of the country, those at the other end of the world, are happy and supplied. We never feel prosperity complete with ourselves alone. Not until the last family has it shall we feel that it has fully come. It is the human instinct for sharing.

We believe that regulating wages on the cost of living is only a way of putting into effect a kind of slavery. It is an utterly illogical method, for the standard by which you measure is thereby made to depend on the thing measured: that is, your standard of living is determined by wages in the first place; to make it in turn the measure of the wage you will pay, is simply to invent another most vicious circle. In determining our wage rates we do not concern ourselves in the least with the cost of living. We have no data on the cost of living among our employees and we do not want any. We only hope that the standards are high and growing higher. The wages we pay are based not on the cost of living but on the value of production. There is no other basis for wages. "Cost of living" is a phrase which means nothing unless it is understood in relation to the standard of living. If the standard is high, the cost is high. But before either standard or cost can go up, wages must go up. The standard of living is fixed by the wages.

The whole question of wages will in the end be worked out by the amount of skill that is required from the workers. This will be the measure of their productivity through machines. The requirement for skill is constantly increasing in the shops so that to-day a man in a shop is usually better off than a man in an office. Workers at machines need a higher grade of skill than the routine men in an office, while tool makers must have a very high grade of skill indeed. This is gradually but surely destroying the advantage of the white collar, and soon we shall have our brightest young men seeking the shops rather than the offices. Brains are becoming so necessary in shops that it is considered good business to pay very highly for them, and there will no longer be the artificial social distinctions between the man who works at a desk and the man who works at a machine.

We are not beyond the creeping stage in business. When business learns to walk then we shall begin to learn something more about wages and probably destroy the lines that to-day separate wages and salaries. Every large business to-day pays salaries which fifty years ago would have been thought impossible—the owners then regarded all their employees simply as so many hired men who ought to be glad that they had jobs at all. There is every reason to believe that with better organization wages will travel in the same direction—provided always that we never have the foreign idea planted among us to the effect that a wage earner should think of himself as a wage earner and utterly dependent upon the will of someone for a job.

Everything that has been said here is taken from our own experience with wages. During 1910 we paid an average hourly rate of 25 cents. This dropped 2 cents in

1911 but in 1913 stood at 26½ cents. On January 12, 1914, we made effective the $5.00 per day minimum rate. This raised the average hourly rate for the year to slightly under 60 cents. In 1915 and 1916 the average rate dropped several cents but by 1918 it had risen to 67 cents. On January 1, 1919, we raised the minimum daily rate to $6.00. This made the hourly rate for that year 77 cents. It reached nearly 86 cents during the inflation of 1920 and in 1921, adding in the bonus then paid, reached 87½ cents. During 1922 the rate was slightly under 80 cents but this was actually a much larger wage than in the two previous years because its purchasing power was greater. During 1923 the average was above 82½ cents per hour and in the following year this increased by a cent and in 1925 decreased a cent. In 1926 the average was over 85½ cents, equalling within a fraction of a cent the wages paid in the inflated currency of 1920. This increased by 10 cents to 95 cents in 1927 and decreased 5 cents during 1928. For 1929 the average was a little less than 92½ cents and then on December 1, 1929, we increased the minimum to $7.00 a day. This brought the average hourly rate for January and February, 1930, to a fraction over $1.00.

That is, during twenty years our average hourly rates have quadrupled. Our present average hourly rate about equals the daily rate for unskilled labour in 1910—for at that time a dollar for a ten-hour day was considered a fair wage. During this period our costs of manufacturing have steadily decreased so that to-day it costs us less than half as much to make a finely and accurately machined piece of highly specialized material than it did in 1910 to make a comparatively crude piece out of comparatively crude material. These are facts and therefore it is not necessary to speculate on whether or not high wages can be paid.

If wages have been multiplied by four in twenty years then they can be multiplied by more than that during the next twenty years. It was generally accepted in 1910 that industry had reached a high state of perfection and there were those who were inclined to sit back and view it with extreme satisfaction. There are those who think that the industry of 1930 has reached a high state of perfection and who also are inclined to view it with satisfaction. These wages have been made possible not by forcing the worker—for he does less hard work to-day than he did twenty years ago—but by new processes, machines, and materials. With this twenty-year accumulation of knowledge, American industry should be able to progress much faster in the next twenty years. Therefore wages can be expected to increase in the future at an even more rapid rate—provided the leaders of industry actually lead. If wages do not continue to increase, the fault will be a human one—it will be due to lack of intelligence.

It is never an easy matter to make a considerable increase in wages and at the same time lower prices. The reasons against such a step are always more numerous than the reasons for it. All our wage increases have been voluntary—that is, our men have never asked for a general raise. When we put in the minimum of seven dollars a day it loaded us with an additional wage payment of about twenty million dollars a year, for a raise was given to every one of our workmen regardless of whether he was receiving above or below the new minimum. But within three months the increased interest of the workers, improved machinery and methods, and an increased volume of sales due to the low prices brought our costs to below what they were before the wage increase went into effect.

If one waits to raise wages until a time when the costs become so low that there is a wide margin of profit on the sales prices—then one will wait forever. We have never yet raised wages at a time when the saving of the extra payments was an open-and-shut matter. In our policy no man is ever raised because he asks for more money. We put in automatic raises in pay for each man every six months. By no means all the men improve enough to be worth their higher wages; if a man reaches a point where he is not earning his money, he may be discharged and rehired at a lower rate. Then his pay raises start up again and it is seldom necessary to discharge him a second time, for he learns his lesson and gives value for his pay. Other men are worth the increases they get and keep on steadily advancing. We have a minimum below which no wage can fall. But we have no maximum rate and we do not reduce wages. We are always better off when the men can earn the highest rate we can pay. It is unfortunate that all men will not or cannot do that.

It will be objected that not all services lend themselves to high wages. That is an old story. In manufacturing the first machinery was designed to do the work in almost the same way as it had been done by hand. When we built our first automobiles we thought of them as horseless carriages and we used bodies much like those

of carriages. It took a long while to learn that the automobile is not a horseless carriage. It took a long while to
learn that a paint brush is not necessary in putting on
paint—that the paint may much better be sprayed on. It
took still longer to learn that a machine with interchangeable parts does not have to be made all in one factory and
may be assembled at the point of use. It can be taken
as axiomatic that any job which cannot pay high wages
and discover them to be cheap wages in point of cost of
production is wrong—that the work can be done in some
other and cheaper way.

Gradually and without knowing it we are revising all
our opinions on this subject. There is no reason, for instance, why a garbage collector should not be a first-
class employee. But this end cannot be obtained by simply
paying wages. It can be done only by taking garbage
as a valuable product. We are now doing this at our
British plant—which derives part of its power from burning the garbage of London.

We are increasing in understanding. Nothing, of course,
is so nearly right as it should be. It is foolish to praise
any present achievements as if we had climbed a pinnacle
of progress. But the remedies for what is wrong are not
in the hands of those who most loudly proclaim themselves our social and economic doctors. Politicians and
theorists and sentimental reformers cannot help us. Shack-
ling business with laws will not give us the liberation into
economic freedom which we all desire. Most laws touch-
ing economic affairs are harmful because they try to preserve things as they are—or as they were. The law deals
with a condition which yesterday became intolerable and

which to-day is on its way into oblivion; the law thus made for the correction of yesterday's error is a hindrance to to-morrow's progress. Business changes and becomes better in its method, more social in its outlook, but the old law remains.

Legislation has never created economic progress.

NOTE

FORD AVERAGE HOUR RATES.   MARCH 20, 1930

Month of July, 1910—Highland Park & Piquette	$ .2542	
" " " 1911—Highland Park only	.2316	
" " " 1912— " " "	.2508	
" " " 1913— " " "	.2660	
" " " 1914— " " "	.5988*	
" " " 1915— " " "	.5224	
" " " 1916— " " "	.5364	
" " " 1917— " " "	.6271	
" " " 1918— " " "	.6703	
" " " 1919— " " "	.7742†	
" " " 1920— " " "	.8598	
" " " 1921— " " "	.8764‡	
" " " 1922—Rouge & Highland Park	.7970	
" " " 1923— " " " "	.8266	
" " " 1924— " " " "	.8378	
Avg. for year 1925— " " " "	.8285	
" " " 1926— " " " "	.8579	
" " " 1927— " " " "	.9524	
" " " 1928— " " " "	.9011	
" " " 1929— " " " "	.9242§	
Jan. & Feb. 1930— " " " "	1.0017	

---

* $5.00 per day minimum—effective January 12, 1914.
† $6.00 "   "   "   "   " 1, 1919.
‡   Bonus included in hour rates "   " 1, 1921.
§ $7.00 per day minimum—effective December 1, 1929.

CHAPTER V

UNEMPLOYMENT OR LEISURE?

I T IS often said that the responsibility for unemployment rests with the leaders of industry. This is not quite true. Modern industry itself rests upon useful employment. But it is a certain very definite grade of employment. Merely hiring men and setting them to work at anything and at any kind of wage is not employment in the modern industrial sense. Employment and high wages are so inseparably linked together that the concern which pays low wages to more men is a public menace, a positive barrier to economic progress, as compared with the concern which pays high wages to fewer men. For employment is a matter not of quantity but of quality. Unemployment is usually the result of low-quality employment. In this sense, the industrial leader who creates low-quality employment is directly creating unemployment, and is to blame for it.

Both wages and profits have a broad social effect in sustaining consumption, and consumption sustains industry and industry sustains employment. If the wage link in the chain be weak, the chain will break and the whole machine will stop.

Taking the industrial picture as a whole and from the impersonal viewpoint, the only employment which matters is that at high wages and we shall have to learn to distinguish between leisure and unemployment. We have accustomed ourselves to thinking of a man without work as a man without support—because in the past there has never been any margin in wages to finance leisure. When men commonly worked from ten to twelve hours a day, a concern went on the eight-hour day only during slack seasons. That meant a loss all around. Now the eight-hour day is nearly standard, and men have more than when they laboured longer and earned less. Likewise the time came when men were given work for five days a week only because there was not enough to employ them for six days. In our industries we have established five days as a normal week—making Saturday a full holiday instead of a half holiday. Nowhere to-day is the Saturday half holiday taken as a sign of dull business. It is recognized as a period of leisure and not as a period of unemployment. The general conceptions of leisure and unemployment have already changed. And in attacking the problem of unemployment it is necessary to tread carefully, else leisure and unemployment may be so confused that real unemployment will be brought about.

If the six-day week of twelve-hour days were restored under modern production methods, then shortly we should have a great closing down of shops simply because the people, regardless of their finances, would not have the leisure to consume what was being produced. It is the part of the managers of industry not only so to arrange their affairs as to pay high wages but also to arrange that the workers have leisure—for not otherwise can the wheels be kept constantly turning. Leisure has an important economic phase and is sharply to be distinguished from the idleness of unemployment.

The responsibility therefore for the well-being of the people rests in a larger degree than we have recognized with the leaders of industry—not with the political managers but with the leaders of the daily work of the people. A statesman is one who clears the way for what Almighty God is going to do. But a statesman is not always a member of a political government; he may be merely a director of daily work. We have come to the point where we must recognize and accept the essential statesmanship of industrial leadership. Politics, misguided, has power to prevent progress, but it cannot create prosperity.

For prosperity can come—and this cannot be too often repeated—only by the providing of an abundance of goods at honest values and by so designing the goods and the processes of their production that high wages and low-priced goods may be among the results achieved. Thus business must be considered as something very much more than a method of earning a living. It is also one of the forces that shape the nation's life.

The leaders of business are as responsible for the welfare of the people as the generals of an army are responsible for the welfare of the soldiers. Also the leaders of business are responsible to one another. For everything is interdependent. I do not mean to say that the leaders of business are either the guardians or the overlords of the people. They are servants, else their tenure is very short. Their responsibility has to do with continually seeing to it that their activities are beneficial to the people as a whole. A big business never becomes big by being a narrow society looking after only the interests of its organization and stockholders.

What we call prosperity in this country is simply the more general distribution of the national income through industry. The extent and usefulness of that national income have been brought about by the use of machine power to cheapen the cost of the production of goods and at the same time distribute higher wages. Under the old conditions the output was of necessity so low and so many men had to be employed in the process that wages also had to be low. We can increase prosperity only as we increase production. If we increase the number of men employed without also increasing the production, we have not increased employment at all, we have only diluted it, for we must divide the amount available for wages in any company by the number of men and, if the production drops per man, the wages of all will, of course, drop.

This fact becomes of high importance to unemployment, for, if more men are at work than the jobs in hand call for, then we may be much worse off than if a number of men are employed at good wages and the others are either not employed at all or otherwise employed—for these latter are at least not destroying employment by diluting it. For instance, back in 1919-1920 too many men were being employed for the work there was to do— there was no industrial leadership and everyone was madly after wages or profits instead of work. Prices went very high and then almost overnight business stopped. The wages at the time were supposedly high because they contained a great number of dollars, but prices were so high that the wages had little buying power and hence were really low. The lack of industrial direction caused too many men to be employed, and since costs were not watched naturally prices had to go up.

The number of men employed at any one time on a given amount of work is thus by no means an indication of the state of industrial prosperity. It may be a sign of coming trouble. It cannot be too often repeated that industry as a department of human activity does not exist merely to support men—its primary purpose is to create goods that will serve the people.

It seems to be taken for granted, however, that spreading the work of a factory over six months when that same work might be better done in three months is somehow making work for men—that it is preventing unemployment. That is not so. Any plan which comprehends doing work in less than the best way and in the least time will only in the end decrease the number of men employed at wages high enough to make them consumers.

The trouble in all this is that everyone is talking about the wrong thing. It is not employment or unemployment that matters. It is work that is of consequence. The progress of the work in any industry may be interrupted by:

(1) Seasonal demand for the product—only a few products are consumed equally during twelve months of the year.

(2) The closing of a factory to make changes in the design of the product or of the machinery. These changes may also involve the employing of more men or of less men according to the circumstances.

(3) The general depression of industry due to one or more of a number of causes.

The thought is quite general that if work, and consequently employment, were not interrupted by any of the above causes—or if indeed it were not interrupted at all—we should have an even flow of prosperity. The cry is to stabilize. The programme in many respects seems to be attractive—any programme is attractive which holds the promise of an easy future. Social reformers invariably promise a life of ease and plenty if only their formulas are adopted. If, however, we accept the possibility of stabilizing industry and therefore employment, do we also know the exact condition that we desire to stabilize? Have we as yet had any condition which, all things considered, is so good that we can ask nothing more than to continue it forever? Or is the general desire to sit amid peace and plenty and at the same time to progress to a still higher condition? Is that possible? Is permanency in the nature of things? And how great a price are we willing to pay for it?

And what is to be considered as *steady* work? There are jobs which offer steady employment of fifty-two weeks a year, seven days a week, and ten hours a day, but there is no insistent demand for such jobs. There is no question that these would be steady jobs! Who is going to decide how many hours a day and how many days a week and how many weeks a year make a job steady?

' Obviously no one can decide this. No one has ever decided how long the day's work should be. Machinery did the deciding and we have the eight-hour day only because we have been steadily cutting off the hours through the use of machinery. The eight-hour day has no force of reasoning behind it. Eight is not a kind of sacred cubit.

Someone brought forth the notion that eight hours marked a good night's sleep and so custom has now divided the remaining hours of the day into two parts—eight hours for work and eight hours for relaxation. The division is convenient but it has no scientific basis. If the day be made too short, time required in merely getting to and from work becomes disproportionate and rather than make the day shorter in our own industries we took a day off the working week. Is a job less steady because it calls for five days a week instead of six or seven?

The present length of the working day and of the working week has been a development. In the future it may be feasible to work fewer days a week or again it may prove best to work steadily six days a week for some months and then stop. The only point on which one can now be certain is that we do not as yet know enough to fix any working period as exactly right—and I doubt if we shall ever know enough to do that. It may well be that some sections of industry are better off working on the highly seasonal basis and that the trouble is not with the industry but with the men who look for a year's support from an industry which can give only half a year's support. If an industry or any industrial unit can work steadily through the whole year so much the better, but the steady work through the year must not be gained by spreading the work and also the wages thin. Nothing is to be gained and a great deal may be lost by thinking in that direction.

It is not in the eventual interest of the wage earner and hence not in the interest of society ever to make work in order to retain unneeded men. The sentiment may be sound but the method is false in that it works an economic wrong in the hope of protecting an economic right. Both the employers and the workers must be made independent and the thought must be downed that industry exists to support people. We have been forced in some emergencies to depart from this policy. We have had to spread work among a number of men, giving each man a few days a week. But we regard it as a makeshift, and surely in this scientific age industry ought to be through with makeshifts. We ought at least to be as proficient in organizing human livelihood on as secure a basis as our coördination of various lines of shop supply. The home, to say the least, should be on as sound a basis as the factory. Every makeshift suggested by our sympathy is another proof of the present insufficiency of our science.

A make-work policy is most insidious and will creep in under many names. A company will construct buildings which it does not need—just to employ men in the construction. A city will embark on hastily considered, badly planned, crudely executed public works for the sake of the reputation of having employed the workless. I am not saying that these things are wrong, but they certainly spring from roots of wrong and by their fruits we may know them. The employment of men at useless tasks is only bringing about a condition worse than the one which is sought to be avoided. The best that can be said is that it is doubtless cheaper to meet emergency conditions in some charitable manner than to give charity under the guise of work. Neither course, however, is necessary.

There is plenty of work for everyone and it is not possible for any man to do useful work without in some fashion receiving adequate payment. I have often thought that if the jobless who are at times in the big cities would set to work at work they see everywhere waiting to be done, they would quickly find that they had made good jobs for themselves. The work is always there, but what men wait for is employment. It is not their fault; they have been taught for ages that it is employment and not work that counts. An employer is usually a man who has tackled the work; an employee is usually a man who is satisfied with the security of a job on another man's work.

More men seek wages than seek work. If work be put first, then we shall get somewhere—for the amount of work to be done is always unlimited. The amount of work to be done never fails—only the money to pay for work seems to fail. But the money will not fail if the mind be constantly on the work instead of on the wages or the profits. The work will then provide both the wages and the profits.

In the Ford industries we are steadily trying to put the work first. Inside the shops we have the best conditions that we know how to create, we make the jobs as economical of human energy as we know how to make them, and we pay the best wages that we know how to pay. But we do nothing at all outside the shops except when it is demonstrated that our employees are being imposed upon or otherwise exploited by some group. Then we aid in getting rid of that as we would aid in fighting a pestilence. In the shops we for years had a system of transfers by which a man who did not like his job could make application for a shift to some other job. This plan was an experiment in keeping men satisfied. But we have abandoned that plan, for we found that some men had great stacks of transfers and that instead of searching for jobs that better fitted them they were searching for jobs without work. And since we have no such jobs we simply abolished the transfer system. Now if a foreman sees that a man is not fitted for the work he is doing, he sends him to the office to receive another job. This is simply putting the work first. And it seems to give more general satisfaction than the old transfer plan.

In the ordinary course of a progressive business, machines and jobs must be continually shifting. These changes displace men and if the men displaced have viewed their jobs as ends in themselves then they are sure to suffer hardship—and this will continue until they gain a different point of view. A job is not in the nature of a permanent endowment. It is an opportunity to gain experience in a certain kind of work and the man in the job ought to be pressing forward to make further use of the experience he is gaining. It only makes for eventual poverty to regard a man in a job as a dependent who must be kept in his job, or to regard a specific job as something that must be retained because a certain man occupies it. That can be done in politics but it cannot be done in business. Customers are freer to retaliate than are taxpayers.

In our industries we have steadily increased the total number of men employed but have steadily decreased the number of men employed per unit of output. Our problem is to get first-class men who are capable of earning high wages and each shift that we make gives an opportunity for sifting out men. We recently abolished a whole department that employed six hundred and fifty men. Of these men we absorbed more than five hundred and fifty in other departments. The other hundred were men who we felt would be better off in another industry. It is not helping anyone to encourage the belief that a workman or a salaried man is entitled to a living out of any certain job regardless of what he does. The responsibility is on the employer to pay the very highest wages he can arrange. The responsibility is on the employee to make certain that he is not being overpaid—for a wage that is simply accepted cannot long continue. It has to be earned and this applies equally whether the wage be one dollar or one hundred dollars a day.

If a shift in the business has to be made or if any extensive changes have to be made, they ought to be made as quickly and as sweepingly as possible and without regard to other than the general welfare. The immediate welfare of everyone affected is of course of moment, but the interests of the few cannot be protected at the expense of the many. Stopping production to make changes need not always involve a very general unemployment but rather a shifting of jobs—for a great number of men are required to make the changes. When we discontinued the production of Model T and made sweeping changes (which are described in Chapter IX) in order to produce a different kind of product, we might have extended our changes over a longer period. In that case the unemployment would have been just as great, but it would have been so distributed that it would not have been noticed by outsiders. However, it would have been harder on the men, for it would have been longer drawn out. As things worked out, we are using, directly and indirectly, as a result of our complete changes, more men than at our highest previous peak. And we are supplying work for 5,200 American concerns besides our own. That, I believe, is sufficient proof that the public has gained—and we also —by attacking the problem as entire instead of temporizing.

If a thing must be done it is well to do it and get it over with.

Our experience has been that the permanent displacing of men by machinery is not a fact. The phrase "technological unemployment" has been invented to cover this condition and, while no one has suggested that improvements in machine equipment should not be made, it has been seriously suggested that the machine which once created more jobs by reason of the increased business which cheap production made possible, is now actually displacing more men than business in general can reabsorb. It is not claimed that this is a sudden thing, for it is not possible to make changes quickly enough to displace any considerable number of men suddenly. But the slow increase in the numbers of displaced men over a considerable period is cited as the commencement of something serious. Now, it may be possible to show that in manufacturing plants there has been, say, something like a one per cent. decrease in employment annually over the past seven years. And unless one knows the manufacturing does not constitute the nation's largest employment opportunity, the figures are impressive. But surely the American, above all men, should realize that manufacturing is just the fountain of hundreds of forms of employ-

ment not remotely related to manufacturing. Industry is
only the starter on the employment machine. The making
of automobiles has created scores of kinds of employment
which have nothing to do with automobiles. In a town of
eight hundred people, an industry employing sixty people
at modern wages would create many kinds of employment
for the rest of the town. So, when considering employment, you must look beyond the industrially employed,
because the chief usefulness of industry to our economic
situation is that it is not a whirlpool sucking all into itself,
but a geyser constantly giving out: it has created more
jobs outside industry than it has inside. That is a healthy
condition. If progress displaces men in industry, all right.
That same industry has already created places for them
outside. These things are clear once they are analyzed.
The difficulty is that we talk so much about industry we
forget that it is only one form, though a very important
form, of American activity. Technological displacement
is quite a different thing from technological unemployment. And I would hazard the guess that unemployment
is more common where there is no technological displacement than where there is. Our own experience is directly
contrary to what the theorists say. Our employees have
increased in number and our payroll in amount, and even
then we have to let work out. In 1929 we were giving
work to 2,200 concerns; this year we constantly use 3,500
concerns out of a total of 5,800 who supply us. Work is
spreading instead of contracting. That is the paradox of
economy. Our products have made at least ten or twenty
times as much employment outside of our company as
they have in it and the lower we price our product and

consequently the more we produce, the more useful jobs
outside are created. I am referring not to the jobs in the
chain of production nor to the jobs created in the servic-
ing, the supplying, and in the use of the finished thing—
but to all the business consequent upon a mobile public—
that is, the car on the road. The automobile industry is in
itself an answer to the emotional belief that machines permanently displace men.

It is often asserted that in dealing with this whole subject of providing useful and therefore remunerative work
for men we only need more facts. That is only partially
true. We need more facts—but they must be universal
facts, and not only the facts of a local or temporary situation and not the confirmation of traditional errors. But
we need more than facts. We also need vision. For facts
may be merely paving stones, but vision is the road—a
road first trodden by the pioneer and afterward paved by
the plodder. Not that facts and vision are opposed to
each other, but the value of facts depends entirely on our
vision of them. We never go forward on known facts: we
learn the facts afterward. The world is the fundamental
fact. How little we should ever have known of it had we
not gone forward on faith! But those of us who spend our
days getting and giving experience do need facts. And
also we need some rather special thinking apparatus for
discarding as fact that which has ceased to be true.

A fact is a changeable thing. By the time anyone has
assembled a large collection of facts on any subject the
value of the facts has usually so changed with their number and new relations that the facts are only records of
the past and not guides for the present. I doubt if actually

anyone has ever assembled all the facts on anything without in the process changing the character of every fact he possessed before.

The value of facts cannot be overestimated—if they be properly used. But falsehood masquerading as facts or facts used without imagination or discrimination are wholly destructive.

The affairs of our people in general would be greatly benefited if our business men were better readers of the signs of the times. To be a business man is to assume the responsibility of economic leadership. When a man undertakes a business in his community he virtually says: "I am taking upon myself part of the direction of your economic life, just as the physician takes upon himself part of the direction of your health, and the schoolmaster part of the direction of your children, and the minister part of the direction of your attitude toward spiritual realities."

If the physician were to urge upon his people every medical vagary, if the schoolmaster were to supply the trivialities more than the essentials, if the clergyman were to make confusion, extravagance, and irresponsibility the end of his calling, everyone would feel that these men were outraging their professions. It is exactly the same when the business man does foolish things. He has more opportunity to do harm than anyone else, because his contact with the people is constant, while that of the others is only occasional.

It is, therefore, part of the business man's duty to his community to read the signs of the times so that he may be a good and helpful leader of his people in their economic interests. He has no more right to mislead them, to lure them into wrong practices, than has the clergyman, the doctor, or the schoolmaster. As things are, however, the local business men are the agents on whom the inventors of wrong economic practices depend for their popularization and spread. No wrong economic practice, no disastrous system of doing business, could possibly get a foothold except through the local business man.

We are learning that a business to be successful— which is another way of saying to be of the highest service —must be in a position to control not only its prices and its wages but also its profits, and that it is the primary duty of management. An entirely new conception of business in all its relations is on the way. We are growing out of little business with all its little thoughts.

Service is the foundation of successful business. But the word has taken on so many meanings and so often is used in such a cheap way that it is beginning chiefly to be used for the masking of hypocrisy.

That a business must be devoted to the service of mankind is entirely beyond the comprehension of the man who sees things only from day to day and cannot see business or anything else in its larger aspects.

The only difficulty that anyone will meet through an absolute devotion to service in business has to do with profits. These will be embarrassingly large. Following the policy of service means directing a business instead of permitting it to be directed by outside forces. And until a man is master of his own affairs he is not really in business. A man is scarcely in business if he makes a product no better and no worse than do his fellows, pays the going rates of wages, and sells at the market prices. He may own his plant, but he does not own his business. To follow a policy of service a business must have leadership that is willing to work and to think. Then service will go through every part of the business. It will design the product and its making, sell at its own prices, and pay its own wages. Inevitably it will control its own finances. And unless the finance of a business comes about as the result of its own progress—no matter what may seem to be its condition —it is heading backward and not forward.

The continued success of any business is not the result of a series of lucky accidents. Plain luck may make a company apparently successful for a time, but as a business matures there need be in it no uncontrolled factors. Some outside factor such as war or political interference may change or check the progress, but otherwise a business can be its own master to a very large degree. If a dozen of the largest companies in this country were to act together in certain essentials, then it would be clearly possible to prevent those hard times that come, not through necessity, but through departing from the fundamentals of service, and particularly from that fundamental of always giving value. The first sign of approaching hard times comes when prosperity seems so great that short-sighted manufacturers either lower quality or, which is more usual, raise prices in the hope of taking advantage of an undiscriminating public. The men who do this are the first to run to cover and cry hard times when the public discovers that it is being cheated and stops buying.

There is little excuse in this generation for what we call

bad times. There is none at all for abject poverty. Everything that man can use is in the world waiting to be taken. All that is left for man is to extract, convert, and distribute those things that Nature has provided. And yet when man falls down on this job he complains of bad times, as though they are decreed by a force over which he has no control.

There are directions in which the government can help in preventing periods of widespread unemployment due supposedly to lack of work but actually due to the breaking of the money link between production and consumption. These will be taken up in a later chapter. Such measures can be helpful if they look toward the preventing of waste—waste in transportation, in the generation of power, or in any other direction. But, in the long run, real progress in providing well-paid work for men must come—as it has come in the past—from the insistent pressure by the leaders of business for lower prices and higher wages. As we decrease waste we increase work.

CHAPTER VI

THE VALUE OF LEISURE

IF MACHINES are to be of any utility to man they must do more than make goods. They must provide for fuller and better lives by taking man out of the conditions of the good old times when he had to work from dawn to dusk in order to gain a bare and very hard living.

The machine, rightly managed, must afford the man who runs it enough income to buy what he makes and, further than that, must give him leisure. This leisure also has an important bearing upon the consumption of the goods which the machines make.

In 1914 we raised our minimum wages to five dollars a day; and some years later we raised the minimum to six dollars a day; and late in 1929, after the so-called stock-market crash, we raised our minimum wage to seven dollars a day. Our average wage paid is slightly over one dollar an hour. No wage paid by us is lower than 87½ cents an hour—that is the minimum. A day is eight hours. In September, 1926, we started to cut the working week to five days of eight hours each.

The results have entirely justified each of these changes. The five dollars a day, and after that the six dollars a day, and now the seven dollars a day, wages have paid and so likewise have the eight-hour day and the five-day week.

Each of these changes was at the time said to be revolutionary. They were really only evolutionary and the results of careful thought and experiment. They are but natural steps in machine industry. In announcing the five-day week, I said:

> The country is ready for the five-day week. It is bound to come through all industry. In adopting it ourselves we are putting it into effect in about fifty industries, for we are coal miners, iron miners, lumbermen, and so on. The short week is bound to come because without it the country will not be able to absorb its production and stay prosperous.

Events have fully demonstrated that the five-day week is as productive as the six-day week. The production has not been attained by speeding the men or doing anything of a like foolish nature. The production is the result largely of better methods, increased machine efficiency and the greater interest of the men. We had somewhat less than a full year's trial of the five-day week with Model T, but that was enough to give us ample figures of its worth so that we adopted it as a fixed policy along with the minimum wage, and it has proved more than satisfactory in the making of the new model in which a high degree of accuracy is required. I mention that accuracy again and again because it is at the bottom of the new industry. The efficacy of the five-day week has with us been fully demonstrated. And it is now so far commending itself to American industry as to be on trial in many places. Of course, the full case for the five-day week cannot be proved unless it carries with it a six-day pay. The purpose of the five-day week is not to compel people to live on five sixths of their present income, but to enable them to earn their present income, or more, in five sixths of the time. In order to earn, men must be enabled to earn, and this enablement is the responsibility of management.

The human element in such an arrangement must be considered and from two angles. The first is from the angle of actual as compared to theoretical efficiency, and the second is from the standpoint of creating a leisure to increase the standards of living and through increasing these standards to increase consumption. We have found—as has everyone—that eight hours a day is the limit of efficiently productive time for the average factory worker.

With the five-day week our plan has been not to work on Saturdays and, of course, not to work on Sundays. We take for granted that Sunday is a day set apart. It is the Lord's Day, and I consider it the duty of an employer to give his employees the opportunity to go to church with their families. It is up to them to make use of the opportunity, and we have no Sunday work at all except for watchmen and tenders. But, all other considerations aside, Sunday work pays no better than work after midnight; it is not a day when men want to work in a factory, and even though they put in an appearance they do not do a normal amount of work.

It has now been sufficiently demonstrated to us that the five-day week for men brings better results than the six-day week. Simply on the point of production it is as much better than the six-day week, as the eight-hour day is better than the ten-hour day. The five-day week is therefore a settled policy.

The influence of a shorter working week on consumption is obvious. The industry of this country could not long exist if factories generally went back to the ten-hour day, because the people would not have the time t. consume the goods produced. For instance, a workman would have little use for an automobile if he had to be in the shops from dawn until dusk. And that would react in countless directions, for the automobile, by enabling people to get about quickly and easily, gives them a chance to find out what is going on in the world—which leads them to a larger life that requires more food, more and better goods, more books, more music —more of everything. The benefits of travel are not confined to those who can take an expensive foreign trip. Just as the eight-hour day opened our way to prosperity, so the five-day week is opening the way to a still greater prosperity.

Of course, there is a humanitarian side to the shorter day and the shorter week, but dwelling on that side is likely to distort the view, for then leisure may be put before work instead of after work—where it belongs. Twenty years ago, introducing the eight-hour day generally would have made for poverty and not for wealth. Ten years ago, introducing the five-day week would have had the same result. The hours of labour are regulated by the organization of work and by nothing else. It is the rise of the great corporation with its ability to use power, to use accurately designed machinery, and generally to lessen the wastes in time, material, and human energy that made it possible to bring in the eight-hour day.

The eight-hour day law to-day only confirms what industry had already discovered. If it were otherwise, then the law would make for poverty instead of for wealth. A man cannot be paid a wage in excess of his production. In the old days, before we had management and power, a man had to work through a long day in order to get a bare living. Now the long day would retard both production and consumption. At the present time the fixing by law of a five-day week would be unwise because all industry is not ready for it, but a great part of industry is ready, and within a comparatively short time I believe the practice will be so general in industry that it can be made universal.

It is not necessary to bring in sentiment at all in this whole question of leisure for workers. In the old days those who thought that leisure was harmful usually had an interest in the products of industry. The mill owner seldom saw the benefit of leisure time for his employees, unless he could work up his emotions. Now we can look at leisure as a cold business fact.

There is a profound difference between leisure and idleness. We must not confound leisure with shiftlessness. Our people are perfectly capable of using to good advantage the time that they have off—after work. That has already been demonstrated. Perhaps they do not use their spare time to the best advantage. That is not for us to say, provided their work is better than it was when they did not have spare time. We are not of those who claim to be able to tell people how to use their time out of the shops. We have faith that the average man will find his own best way— even though that way may not exactly fit into the programmes of the social reformers. We do know that many of the men have been building houses for themselves, and have demonstrated in other ways that the thrifty virtues of the forefathers have not been wanting in their sons.

I think that, given the chance, people will become more

and more expert in the effective use of leisure. For few of us have had the chance to learn.

It is the influence of leisure on consumption that makes the short day and the short week so necessary. The people who consume the bulk of goods are the people who make them. That is a fact we must never forget—that is the secret of our prosperity. With the decrease of the length of the working day in the United States an increase of production has come, because better methods of disposing of men's time have been accomplished by better methods of disposing of their energy. And thus one good thing has brought on another.

Where people work longest and with least leisure, they buy the least goods. No towns were so poor as those of England where the people, from children up, worked fifteen and sixteen hours a day. They were poor because these overworked people soon wore out—they became less and less valuable as workers. Therefore, they earned less and less and could buy less and less. Needs are filled only as they are felt. They make themselves felt largely in leisure hours. The man who worked fifteen and sixteen hours a day desired only a corner to lie in and a hunk of food. He had no time to cultivate new needs. No industry could ever be built up by filling his needs because he had none but the most primitive.

It is perfectly proper for the government to step into an industrial situation with laws—provided those laws only establish what experience has already demonstrated to be the best practice. Eight-hour-day laws are now all right because the eight-hour day has been established. But a five-day week law would be unwise at this moment and so also would laws restricting the use of machinery. Any law passed in the belief that it will make work or spread work over more than the usual number of men is an invitation to poverty. And poverty always accepts the invitation. A deal of the poverty abroad may be traced to political make-work laws.

The right use of leisure must be learned by experience. And there was no proper leisure in the old times. There was only idleness. Merely to make a bare living, that is, to provide the things to be currently consumed, such as food and clothing, requires very little time. The mere living is earned very early in the working day. That part of the business is over and done before the morning has well begun. We go far wrong when we say that it requires all the work that we do to earn our living. In these days we require so many more things than a living that a living has become the smallest part of what we earn. But there are a thousand other things that enter into the matter now—all the material necessities, conveniences, advantages, and opportunities of civilization. Our industries are turning these out in quantity, and the individual worker is providing his own share.

We have no leisure class in this country. All the business of the wealthy would not support a single industry. Our buying class is our working class, and our working class must also become our "leisure class" if our immense production is to be balanced by consumption. Besides, it is only just and human and progressive and educational that the people should use what they produce. That, then, is the new basis for leisure. Instead of hurting business it helps it. We seem to forget that business is one half use. If we always produced and never used there could be no business. But when we apportion the time between production and use we are acting in accordance with economic law.

The burden of adjusting these functions so that they support each other falls upon management. There is no charity involved. Leisure, like everything else, must be earned. No one has control of enough of anything in this world to give a constant supply of it to anyone; we must all produce it together. And this means a type of workman who knows the value of both leisure and labour. A man who knows how to employ his free hours well will also know how to employ his working hours to best advantage. The two cannot very well be mixed, but the type of individual who can work with a will is the type that can also play with a will, and in his play he will be using the accumulated production of his labour.

The people with a five-day week will consume more goods than the people with a six-day week. People who have more leisure must have more clothes. They must have a greater variety of food. They must have more transportation facilities. They naturally must have more service of various kinds.

This increased consumption will require greater production than we now have. Instead of business being slowed up because the people are "off work," it will be speeded up because the people will have more leisure to buy and will consume more in their leisure than in their working time. This will lead to more work. And this to more profits. And this to more wages. The result of more leisure will be the exact opposite of what most people might suppose it to be.

Management must keep pace with this new demand—and it will. It is the introduction of power and machinery in the hands of management that has made the shorter day and the shorter week possible. That is a fact which it is not well to forget.

Naturally all services cannot go on the five-day basis. Some must be continuous and others are not yet so organized that they can arrange for five days a week. But if the task is set of getting more done in five days than we now do in six, then management will find the way.

The five-day week is not the ultimate, and neither is the eight-hour day. It is enough to manage what we are equipped to manage and to let the future take care of itself. It will, anyway. That is its habit. But probably the next move will be in the direction of shortening the day rather than the week.

CHAPTER VII

The Problem of Age

THE terror of the man who works for wages has always been age. When he worked by hand he soon burned himself out and was approaching old age at forty. During a large part of the very crude machine age—from which we are now emerging—the work was so hard and required so little skill that an old man was not as productive as a young man. But now in our experience the larger wages and the easier work have greatly lengthened the effective working years of every man, and because of his training and steadiness the older man is to us more useful than the younger man. Indeed, one of our problems is now to see that enough young men are employed to keep up a steady flow of trained people.

Age has never meant anything to me either personally or in my relations with others. We have employed hundreds of thousands of people in the past twenty-five years and have had the opportunity to learn the comparative values of youth and age in a cold dollars and cents way. As a result, we have come to think not at all of age but only of experience and the capacity to learn.

Anyone who stops learning is old—whether this happens at twenty or at eighty. Anyone who keeps on learning not only remains young but becomes constantly more valuable —regardless of physical capacity.

To-day's limitations on the commercial value of a man or woman have nothing at all to do with the number of years lived. There is a place for everyone who is willing to work and to try to go forward. There is no place for anyone who refuses to work or to go forward. It is not enough just to be willing to work. It is not enough just to desire to push forward. The two must be combined, for the one is of no use without the other. Anyone who is satisfied with the progress that he is making or is inclined to be thankful for having arrived at his present position is old.

Having lived a number of years is a great advantage to anyone if those years have brought a background of experience. It is usual to associate age with years rather than with increased experience only because so many men and women somewhere along in what is called middle age stop trying. They let themselves be old. And yet almost all enduring success comes to people after they are forty. For seldom does mature judgment arrive before then.

There is really no problem of age. The real problem is to induce people to use what is in them. I am thoroughly convinced that everyone is capable of doing at least twice as much as he or she is now doing. They need only to be spurred on.

Then there is the kind of man who sincerely thinks that he can do only one sort of work. Some years ago, just after we began to make tractor experiments, I was driving in alone to the factory, and I picked up an elderly man who was carrying an old suitcase and apparently waiting for the trolley car. We fell to talking on the way in, and he asked me if I knew of a good livery stable in Detroit.

"There are not many livery stables now," I told him. "They are going out of style, aren't they?"

"Yes, they have in Ypsilanti where I came from," he answered, "but there are still some in Detroit, and I will try to find one."

"Well," said I, "do you have to have a livery stable?"

"It's the only thing I know how to do," he said. "The last stable in my town closed yesterday, and I'm going to see what there is in Detroit."

We drove on into town, and I suggested that we might find a job for him in the factory. He didn't know about that; the idea was new to him; he rather felt that he had to work around horses. Before we reached the factory he had changed his mind. The employment department placed him, and he has been working ever since and, incidentally, earning several times as much money as he could ever have had in a livery stable. It had never occurred to him that he could do anything other than tend horses. We may smile at him, but you would be surprised to know how many people are just that way. Only it doesn't happen always to be livery stables.

We have thousands of such cases, for ever since it became known that previous experiences did not count with us our factory has been in the nature of a refuge for competent men who were miscast in the first jobs they undertook or who saw their callings vanish. We have clergymen, doctors, lawyers, and every known sort of mechanic and craftsman working at the machines; in fact, we have never yet wanted any kind of specialist that we have not been able to find simply by looking over the employment cards. These men have made good with us. They could have made equally good somewhere else, but they were afraid to try —they had thought they could not apply for any job without a record of experience.

A very considerable proportion of all men and women find it more profitable to be employed by someone than to start anything on their own account. There is no general rule. Some people are at their best when working on their own account, while others—and probably the majority—are at their best when under direction. The one class has not more ability than the other. It is not so much a matter of ability as of temperament. Some men will assume ten times the responsibility for an employer that they would assume for themselves. Other men and women dodge responsibilities of every kind from the very moment that they start working. Every so often one hears reports that this or that corporation is refusing to hire men or women over forty, and then comes a crop of newspaper articles about the serious problem of the man or woman who needs a job but cannot get it because he or she is over forty. Every two or three years we are surprised to learn that not only are we refusing to hire anyone over forty but that we are discharging those who have reached that age. For the past ten or fifteen years we have not even bothered to contradict these reports.

In point of fact, we should prefer, if we could make the choice, to have all of our people between thirty-five and sixty years old, for then we should have a stable and experienced force. We should not care how much over sixty the men were so long as they could do their work. Under no circumstances would we have a working force made up only of young men. It is absolutely necessary, in order to get the work through, to have a solid framework of older and more experienced men who know exactly what they are doing. Not long ago in the laboratory at Dearborn I wanted to find out about some work that was being done. The man who told me everything that I wanted to know, and in clear, quick fashion, was a white-haired, slightly stoop-shouldered man. He was the keenest man in the group and was just as alert physically as he was mentally. I asked him his age, and he said he was seventy-four.

It is not to be expected that a man of seventy will have as much endurance as one of twenty-five. It is not at all necessary that he should have, for by the time a man has reached seventy he ought to have something a great deal more valuable than physical strength. However, the records of the employment department show that the work which calls for endurance is best served as a rule by men who are forty and over. Younger men seem to tire of jobs of this kind rather quickly and want to be transferred to lighter work.

The reason why employment cannot be restricted to men or women over thirty-five is that a certain number of younger men must be taken on for training, and also because a large employment roll ought to be as nearly as possible a cross-section of society. Recently on a day when the factory count was 92,208 men, of whom all but 1,477 were on day rate, the ages and number of men at each age were as follows:

From 18 to 20 years old	1,233 men
" 21 " 30 " "	25,213 "
" 31 " 40 " "	34,585 "

From 41 to 50 years old	21,764 men
" 51 " 60 " "	6,600 "
" 61 " 70 " "	1,257 "
" 71 " 73 " "	57 "
" 74 " 83 " "	22 "

This we believe is a fairly representative cross-section of society. It will be noted that we employ considerably more than twice as many men above thirty as under thirty and that the largest group is between thirty-one and forty. The group above forty, however, is larger than the group below thirty. We have more men over sixty than we have under twenty. These figures do not bear out the impression that forty or any other age constitutes a dead line of employment. [NOTE: For the arrangement according to ages see the table at the end of this chapter.] In fact our employment department makes no age distinctions whatsoever. Fitness to the work is the only requirement. The older man would probably be assigned to a somewhat slower job than the younger man—that is about the only difference one would notice. We expect the younger men to be faster than the older men, and this generally—although not always—turns out to be the case. Some of our fastest men—by which is meant men who can handle certain kinds of light work very quickly—are around fifty.

Our experience with women workers is not large—although it is considerable. We have no objection to the employment of women, but only a small portion of our work is suited to them, and we also have the very definite policy of not employing any women who do not have others dependent on them. On the whole I share the feeling that women's least valuable contribution to life is made through industry.

The whole question of age does not seem to me to be important. Age is not so much a bar to the old as it is to the young, and more especially to the young boys.

The only jobs freely open in most places to boys without experience are dead-end jobs at low wages. If the job has a future, then the boy is expected to start at almost nothing a week. How he is to live, how he is to stop being a normal boy and turn drudge, has apparently concerned no one. We penalize the boy for his lack of experience. We ought to penalize ourselves for that lack.

A boy just out of school is not experienced in any line of work. What he learns in school does not fit him for work and especially for mechanical work. Often he comes out with a strong prejudice against work and particularly against any work where he cannot wear a white collar. The education he is supposed to get does not seem to take. That is one of the reasons why we started our trade school—of which more will be told in a later chapter.

We take no stock in this talk about boys and girls having degenerated. They are no crazier to-day than ever they were—it may be that they have more sense than they used to have. Certainly the girls have more sense, for they have more freedom and thus greater opportunity to gain sense. Some people seem to think that they dress queerly and act queerly. We think they are dressing sensibly and that they are brighter and more able to take care of themselves than ever they were.

Just putting these boys to work is not enough. No kind

of useful work is degrading, but one kind of work may morally be more helpful than another kind. Accurate work has a morality all its own. We want to teach these boys accurate work and pay them well for it. Then, we believe, the immorality of crime will not have to be preached to them. For crime will then show up for what it is—a very hard and footless way of trying to get money.

It would help if our educators should discover something about industry and change the direction of education toward it instead of away from it. For a long time it was felt that one who went in for books was entering the "learned" world, while one who went in for machinery was entering a lower plane of living. Only a few are even now realizing the vast amount of learning which underlies mechanics, the incessant research and experiment its development demands, the precise knowledge of natural law involved in all its processes, and the endless exploration by scientific outposts.

This is the age of accuracy. It is the age of good work. We measure time in smaller fractions than before and can now do much more with our day. On every hand there is accuracy and a demand for more accuracy and an increase of the technical means of obtaining accuracy—as was discussed in the earlier chapters.

Accurate planning for accurate work has another and very important human side. The work and the jobs are all planned, and thus they can be divided into classes according to the skill and strength required in each. In other words, an industry begins to have jobs which can be graded according to the degrees of age, ability, and experience within a community. That is, the roster of jobs in an industry can and ought to represent a cross-section of a community.

However, every class of human beings except one gets a chance to earn a living. Whether or not the chance is accepted is another matter. The one class that does not get a chance, regardless of ability or of actual performance in a job, is made up of those men who have been in jail. It is somehow considered highly virtuous to have nothing at all to do with a man who has been jailed; men who are trying to make good are discharged once their records are uncovered. And of course they are driven back to crime. Those are the men who need help and who do not get it.

We have done our best to help by not asking any questions or making any record of where a man has worked before. We do not care anything about references, and a man is kept or discharged solely on his record with us. That record we do keep. From time to time men have came straight from jail to some of us, told their stories, and asked for jobs. Most of those men we manage to place and not even the employment department knows that they have prison records, for we never send a man to the employing office to be given a job on the ground that he is a reformed or about-to-be-reformed criminal. He is sent down as a friend that we should like to see placed and that is all there is to it. The man stands on his own feet and nearly always he becomes a valuable employee—once he has gained his self-respect and the knowledge that he is not going to be hounded for anything that he has done in the past. I recall one man who came to me after several years in jail. I asked him if he was living with his wife and he said, somewhat embarrassed, that he was not. I told him that he would have to go back to his wife.

"Yes," he said, hesitating, "but that is the trouble. That is why I was sent up. You see, I shot her in a row."

That just made the cast more interesting. We put him in a job, and then he had a relative who needed a job, and finally we got him all squared up at home, and he has been working for us for many years now. There are many such odd cases but we know of them only in a personal and not at all in an official way, for the facts are not of record. An official of Detroit once asked us to give him a list of all men in our employ who had served prison terms. We told him to come and get it if he could.

The ex-convict trying to keep out of trouble and earn a living generally has a hard time of it. He has a real case. But the men or women who talk about age as a bar to work are usually making an excuse to avoid work. They may convince themselves that they are sincere—it is not hard to fool one's self—but actually they are not so anxious to work as they claim to be. For otherwise they would forget all about age and pitch in and get work.

NOTE

THE AGE DISTRIBUTION AT THE RIVER ROUGE PLANT ON FEBRUARY 20, 1930.

Age	Number of Men	Age	Number of Men
18	46	50	1398
19	538	51	1046
20	649	52	992
21	771	53	816
22	1271	54	710
23	2530	55	714
24	2442	56	574
25	2161	57	558
26	2687	58	448
27	2968	59	385
28	3285	60	357
29	3406	61	293
30	3692	62	213
31	3196	63	176
32	3214	64	147
33	3347	65	111
34	3535	66	94
35	3632	67	72
36	3688	68	52
37	3791	69	51
38	3366	70	48
39	3406	71	24
40	3410	72	19
41	3062	73	14
42	2952	74	3
43	2522	75	4
44	2501	76	3
45	2420	77	5
46	1992	78	4
47	1852	79	1
48	1627	82	1
49	1438	83	1
		Total	90,731
		Salary men	1.477

No. of men on each shift

	Day Rate	Salary
No. 1	12,119	21
No. 2	49,325	1,419
No. 3	29,287	37
	90,731	1,477

Factory count 92,208

CHAPTER VIII

Toward Abolishing Poverty

THE boom philosophy has so infected our business thinking that it is uncommon to find anyone discussing business affairs except in terms of prosperity and depression. It seems to be impossible to think of business except as in one or the other of these extremes. People seem to feel that business must attain increasingly high pressure, or something is wrong. It is not so when they discuss their water supply. It is a good water system that supplies the community's need for water in the quantity and at the time the water is required. We don't talk about boom and depression there. Continuous and sufficient supply is enough. And what is business but a supply of other commodities?—none of them to be compared in vital importance with water. Our work of supplying the needs of the world very often does not get done because attention is distracted by our philosophy of booms and depressions.

One of these days I hope the politicians will cease making capital out of business conditions. They will not cease doing so, however, until the leaders of business cease trying to gain what they imagine to be business advantages through the aid of politicians. It does not make much difference whether the politicians paint the picture so rosily as to induce people to believe that they can gain their living without work or whether they paint it so darkly as to induce people to believe that there is no use working. The net result is the same—the minds of the workers are taken off the real task.

When the boom spirit is on, people are led into extravagance and then into debt, and then into gambling in the hope of somehow getting quick money to release them from the economic predicament brought on by extravagance and debt. When the reaction comes the expenditures go as far below the normal line of need as they went above it during the boom. And so it comes about that the business of this country has had very little experience with anything in the nature of normal progressive consumption.

That is worth considering. It is quite clear on looking back that we have had sufficient experience with extravagance, debt, and speculation. But more is clear than we like to confess, namely, that the people had to be initiated into the degrees with economic error; the doors had to be thrown open and inducements to enter had to be offered; and the r'ole movement took place under the auspices of American business. The people can be no more extravagant than business induces them to be: they can go no further into debt than business permits them to go: they can gamble only when business— or something that passes under that name—provides the opportunity. Let that be candidly and seriously considered, and then let us ask if this great power of business for social education and social leadership cannot be used to build up a system of normal, continuous, and progressive supply and consumption which will replace the periodically collapsing system under which we have been working. We cannot blame the "times": the times have causes. We cannot forever discuss prosperity and depression: these things are symptoms and our usual kind of prosperity is not even a good symptom.

A need implies the supplying of a deficiency. A nation's needs are determined by the nation's civilization. The needs in America are great because America is, in a material sense, highly civilized. And as a nation ascends the ladder of material civilization its needs increase.

The matter of individual needs must be left to the individual. It is for him to determine just what constitutes a necessity for himself. His reckoning must be based on his logical ability to pay, on the use to which he will put the article, and on whether that use is a matter of the present or the future.

When people are led to buy things they do not need and cannot afford, an artificial prosperity is created. Purchasing beyond ability to pay and beyond the need to use brings about the exchange of non-essential goods in great volume and a dangerous expansion of debt. When the natural reaction arrives, people become panicky. Those who have been buying beyond their limits swing far below the line of common sense and refuse to buy even ordinary essentials. This sudden withdrawal of purchasing power affects all classes of industry. There can be only one result. Business becomes stagnant, factories are closed, men are thrown out of work. And all because a certain normal and ascertainable balance was destroyed, not by the "times," but by misdirected and often brilliant business effort.

Just as many people need things as ever. Just as many need the work. Yet because of some miscalculation, or rather, utter lack of calculation, the connection between producing and consuming is broken and everybody suffers. The responsibility does not lie entirely with the producer —though he must as the leader bear a large share of the blame—and the purchasing public must share it with him—but the emphasis now is upon the responsibility of business.

Business in the old manner was always cowardly. It was afraid. It was even afraid to admit that the weather could be bad. Any big newspaper office will furnish stories of protests made by merchants against news items announcing that rain could be expected to-morrow or that a cold spell was coming for Saturday.

The superstition of the business man has been that if he would only call business good, business would be good. A loud booster was an optimist; a true reader of the signs of the times was a pessimist. And instead of doing anything to correct the condition of business this kind of man just keeps on talking until there is no business left to talk about.

The statistics that pretend to show the condition of the country are often unreliable, since they cannot distinguish between sound business and unsound business. Sound business is that in which goods change hands and are paid for. Unsound business is that in which goods are forced out for the sake of keeping up the appearance of movement and are not paid for. And it is always possible so to stimulate the apparent business of any company to a point where it can be presented before the public as a successful enterprise when really it is failing.

The number of things which are currently cited as making for good business or for bad business is truly extraordinary when the things are viewed by themselves. It is not so extraordinary when they are viewed in their surroundings, for then it is seen that they are expedients to avoid the labour of thinking. It is a natural tendency to do what someone else is doing and to assume that because that someone else seems to be successful it is safe blindly to follow him. That is the fallacy of all systems of management which are offered as recipes for success. No one can draw up a system of operation by which a business can be managed at all times. The best that can be done is to draw up a plan showing what is being done now. To-morrow, having learned something, the tack may change. Modern business is sailing an uncharted sea. It needs managers instead of systems of management—managers whose authority is their knowledge, insight, and clear reading of the signs of the times. Management, as a system, is merely the accumulated precedents which previous managers established in their special set of conditions: the conditions have changed: the precedents are no longer authoritative. What business calls for to-day is not followers of precedent, but makers of precedent: and this can never come from men whose business life comprises sales and profits: it must come from men who see business under the aspect of a social circulatory system of supply. Supply, not salesmanship, is its key-word.

Salesmanship, when it has developed every scheme to get goods into everybody's hands, comes to an end. Business that exists merely to keep a sales force going at what that force wants to do, and in the way it wants to do it, may have a merry time for a period, but it comes to a sudden end.

A common delusion in what is called salesmanship has to do with the selling against a rival instead of to the public. Whenever I hear of a business man gravely discussing what he calls his "competitors," I know that he is not managing his own business, but is being subtly managed by the effect his competitors have upon his mind. If a business be devoted to service it can have no rivals or competitors. A business which takes its ideas from other businesses either through fear or emulation and merely copies them has nothing which can really be called a foundation. I have often said that the time spent in studying one's competitors is time wasted. The time can be more profitably spent in studying one's own product and the needs of the public.

We have never, in settling on our own designs or prices, given the slightest attention to what anyone else was doing in the same field. If we do not know how to better our product, we have simply demonstrated that we have no right to be in business and ought to get out of the way of progress. Any attempt to crush one's rival for the purpose of gaining his business is not only a criminal misuse of power but also a great waste of effort, for someone else is certain to come along and take away the buying public while the competitors are fighting.

The instinct to crush a rival is the pettiest expression of power. He who misuses loses more than he who is misused. It is misuse of power to impede a rival, because it is an interference by one who has no right to interfere.

H

Every man has enough to do in his own field. The great danger of competition that has only the competitor in view is that both competitors sink to the level of an altercation, while the public buys elsewhere. Competition in the sense of rivalry in service is another matter; it is competition with the good of the public in view, and under this form of competition all competitors and the public are benefited. But the crush-my-rival kind is doomed to trip itself for a hard fall.

The abolishing of poverty is, as far as I am concerned, the only end of business which is worth considering. It is from this point of view, and only from this one, that we can see the futility of selfish competition and the utter fallacy of the profit-motive. Once we see the ultimate purpose of business as a factor in the life of man, we are through with all the little twiddling fancies that formerly passed for business wisdom. The abolishing of poverty is the only legitimate purpose of business, and its accomplishment is not an impossibility unless we imagine that it can be done all at once by edict. The reasons for poverty are highly individual as well as highly social—that is, there are povertyizing influences for which society as a whole is responsible, and others for which the individual is responsible. Business by its methods and purpose may have a very great effect in removing the social causes of poverty, and through its skilful manipulation of ambitions and desires may have an equally beneficial effect on individual causes of poverty. For there is no question of the power for mass suggestion which modern business possesses. But it has not yet been used for the greater ends.

Prosperity can be in a measure controlled and so also can poverty. Poverty can be controlled to the vanishing point. But neither control can come from above. The control must start with the family unit itself in its buying— not in limiting its buying, but in buying wisely and insisting on values.

The foundation of prosperity is the family. Each family is, or should be, its own business manager. The material affairs of a family are as much a business as the affairs of an industrial corporation. Fortunately, a sufficient number of families always know this instinctively or have figured it out for themselves, and they are enough to guarantee the economic stability of the nation. The family that does not keep itself solvent, that unduly mortgages its future for non-essential and non-productive things, not only endangers its own solvency but decreases the margin of safety upon which the nation depends.

Any system of business in which the money lender too conspicuously thrives is not a truly prosperous system. The greater the spread between the supply and the need, the more middlemen squeezed in between production and use, the heavier is the drag on the nation's prosperity. Credit is an admirable device when it lessens the spread, but when it increases the spread it becomes an enemy to economic health.

There is all the difference in the world between investment and debt, and it should be learned. In the end the proper management of the country devolves upon every household, and it cannot be handed over to profiteering finance, for then sales and not supply becomes the motive; and even these sales are not properly sales, but only apparently so, for nothing has as yet been paid for. A transaction in which the purchaser does not really own his purchase because he has not paid for it, and in which the seller is not really quit of his product because he has not collected for it, is not a sale. It is a state of suspense where the buyer has not really got the goods and the seller has not really got the price.

By certain intensive methods of salesmanship, people are made to believe that they want lots of things that they do not need. This is in the end bad business for everybody because the artificial strain put upon the purchasing power reacts upon production and trade receives a blow. Normal buying and normal selling are needed.

It is said that we as a country cannot stand prosperity. But what is there about prosperity that has to be stood? Have we ever really had national prosperity? And should not prosperity be a natural rather than an unnatural condition? Do we worry much about a man not being able to stand good health? It is also said that as a country we have gone so far toward the perfection of production that we are in danger of being swamped in a sea of goods. What is there to all this?

It is well to bear in mind that whether or not we have prosperity depends on the standard used for comparison. If we compare our present condition with past conditions then we have prosperity. If, however, we compare what we now have with what we shall have in the future, then we have hardly scratched the surface of prosperity. For, much as many think we have developed this country, actually we have scarcely begun its development. We have, as yet, scarcely occupied it. We have not even learned what there is in the country to develop. Far from seeing the end of development, we can scarcely see more than a beginning here and there.

And likewise with production. We have made some progress in production, but only one end of it—the shop end. The rest remains to be done. But through our present progress we gain an inkling of how much more we ought to know and eventually will know. Certainly we are as far away from perfection in production as ever we were, for production begins much farther back than we usually think and ends much farther on. Is anything really produced until it has been distributed and consumed and its essence made to serve some valuable human end? Each step takes us on our journey, but the horizon is never nearer.

If people of this country be thought of as arranged in tiers of buying power, then one can get a notion of what has been happening. Not many years ago only the topmost tiers—the wealthy and the near wealthy—had adequate buying power, and there was not really much for them to buy. The lowermost tiers had almost no buying power—they considered themselves lucky to get enough to eat and a place to sleep.

Mr. Edison has truly said that once a man is assured of enough to eat, his wants become unlimited. This is very true. Anyone whose whole struggle is for food is not going to have any thoughts beyond food. But when the getting of food is no longer an anxiety, then wants begin to rise—and to soar. In this country practically no one is just grubbing for food.

We have changed our definition of poverty. It used to

be that no man was poor unless he was starving. Under-nourishment to-day is due more to ignorance in the choice of foods than to the lack of food. Therefore, few of our people are in the condition of not wanting anything. People want things because they want life, and things are the servants of life. At first the wants and the choice are perhaps not discriminating. But as familiarity with plenty becomes widespread, taste and judgment and responsibility appear. The one way to emancipate a people from a crass materialistic state of mind is to give them plentiful material possessions, for materialism grows from lack not from supply.

We have been learning a little to use what we have, and that use has put money into circulation—which means that buying power has been put into circulation. As this circulation widens, it touches tier after tier of the public, and thus the demand for products steadily grows. As we learn more and more about use and the relation of use and waste, this demand will continue to grow. It will diminish only if we sit back and neglect the development of our country in the false belief that already we have developed it, or—worse still—imagine that we are developing it so quickly that nothing will be left for those who come after us.

There never was less likelihood of our exhausting the natural resources of the country than there is to-day, because nowadays all kinds of waste are being reduced to a vanishing point, the same materials are being used over and over again, and new uses are constantly being found for everything we have. Comparatively speaking we are using up less of our resources because we are getting more

use out of what we use. There is to-day so much to be
obtained in the way of by-products from that which was
formerly discarded, that it is often hard to distinguish
between the product and the by-product. For instance,
in our industries we no longer use raw coal as fuel. It is
with us a raw chemical from which we obtain a number
of useful derivatives, some of which serve as fuel. Heat
is only one of the by-products of coal. Through the distil-
lation of refuse wood we obtain values commensurate with
the value of the lumber. There is waste to-day but it is
not the same sort of waste that our forefathers bothered
about. They paid a great deal of attention to the waste
of materials, but none at all to the waste of human beings.
We are coming to an exactly reverse attitude, and we
regard the waste of materials as important only as it represents the waste of human beings, for the waste that we
practise upon the original store of wealth is always repair-
ing itself. The waste material is replaced. The earth never
ceases making what we need and is prepared to fill future
needs of which we have not now the slightest knowledge.
If men waste energy it is lost to them as individuals—
but the great reservoir of energy on which all life draws is
not exhausted.

There is a kind of economy that represents only fear.
It is a reaction to extravagance. Economy is the rule of
half-alive minds. It is better than waste, but it is not so
good as use. Those who pride themselves on their economy
sometimes bristle when it is attacked, as if one of the
virtues had been denounced. But is there anything more
pitiable than a poor, pinched mind spending the rich days
and months squeezing a few coins and paring the necessi-

ties of life to the very quick? Indeed, there are two kinds
of waste: that of the prodigal who throws his substance
away in riotous living, and that of the sluggard who allows
his substance to rot from non-use. In the precious things
of life the strict economizer may be classed with the sluggard. The beauty of the principle of use is that it contains all the advantages of economy and at the same time
gives healthy expression to all the instincts of which waste-
fulness is a diseased symptom. Most people's extravagance is a reaction to severe suppression cf expenditure.
Most people's economy is a reaction to extravagance.
Under the principle of use the broadening experience of
expenditure is obtained, as well as the self-control and
discipline of economizing.

The fearful are forever predicting shortages of this or
that essential commodity—but the shortages never appear
according to schedule. Every so often we are told that the
supply of petroleum can last only a few years. The soil, it
is predicted, will lose its fertility in the course of the
years, and we shall all die of starvation. And thus it goes.
If a group of people decide on the exact day and hour
when the world is to come to an end we do not give credit
to their forecast. But if some man who is called an
economist or a scientist decides that a part at least of the
world is coming to an end—oil, wood, iron—fifty or a
hundred years hence, then his statement is taken as seriously to be considered.

Is it not more to the point to take what we have at its
face value in the expectation that, whenever a shortage
in any commodity develops, a new and better substitute
will be found for it? The country already has so many

substitutes for wood that the lumber men are worried lest the public get too far away from the use of wood. The far future is going to care for itself, anyway, and the best that we can do is to plan for to-day and for the near future. On that basis it is perfectly apparent that we have not begun to make the provision for to-day that it is within our power to make.

The present era of comparative prosperity coincides with the development of automotive transport. That has developed many millions of mobile horsepower and this in turn has caused a start toward rebuilding the country. It is responsible for the making over of thousands of miles of roads and for the building of thousands of new sections adjacent to cities. It has spread out the cities, but also it has brought the farm closer to the town. The single matter of giving people a chance to move about and see the world is an element which of itself would be sufficient to change the character of the people.

The results of this development—at the best only a partial development—give an idea of what may come about with a fuller development. Or, instead of "fuller development," one might say the opening of wider opportunities.

It is not logical to divide the country into agricultural and industrial groups. Industry has already passed west to Chicago and beyond, while the South, which used to know only cotton, is now quickly becoming industrial because it is beginning to use its water resources for the generation of power. The shift is everywhere from wholly manufacturing or wholly agricultural to a balance between the two. If anyone would figure up the production of the small truck gardens, which so many factory workers may now have because of the automobile, the total would undoubtedly be astounding.

We are very gradually learning the meaning of transportation and power and their relation to both industry and agriculture. We now know that if any district be given the two fundamental elements of transport and power it is bound to grow. This is shown by the gradual decentralization of great industries. Industry can centre at the source of raw material and power, or at the market. Industry did centralize around one or the other of these points. That is changing because both these centres are expanding and overlapping, and a centre is almost anywhere an industry wants to settle. This has had the excellent effect of decentralizing industry and enabling it to disseminate its employment benefits through many widely separated communities.

We undoubtedly need more railroads and also we need a very large extension of public roads for automobiles and trucks. The railroads and the trucks are not competitors—as was at first imagined. Each in its sphere feeds the other. The airplane is developing, and it also will have its sphere and will breed business for all other forms of transportation, for it will open up regions that now in point of time are inaccessible. But we have very little provision for the cheap transport of heavy, bulky freight that does not have to get anywhere in a great hurry. We also have large sections of the country that are but thinly peopled because of a lack of transport, of power, and of water.

A waterway gives the cheapest facility for heavy transport. We have an abundance of such waterways. Developing a waterway for transportation fortunately brings benefits in many directions. The first is that the dams and reservoirs required to give a steady depth of water for navigation fit in perfectly with the generation of power by electricity. We now know how to get the utmost out of the water flow and also economically to transport the power over considerable distances. The second benefit arises from the flood control, which is a necessary incident. The rush of waters that causes a flood can be so retained as to provide an even flow in times of drought. The third great reason is that the massing of big bodies of water helps the rainfall and also provides for irrigation.

In any particular case, one of these elements may be much more important than the others, but they all work together. The country already has before it a number of these projects—all of which have been hanging for years, not because their merits are disputed and not because the necessary engineering skill or the necessary money is lacking, but because all of the projects require a clearing of the way by the national government in coöperation with state governments.

There are a few projects that might at once be undertaken and concerning which engineering opinion is practically agreed, except for what are not much more than details. Their cost is not important. We have the money. And from a national standpoint they should not be looked at in terms of dollars spent but rather in terms of dollars circulated. For these projects alone ought to start enough money into circulation to give employment to anyone who will work, and thus to move up another tier of people into the region of larger buying power. For, while the actual building will be far from the present centres of trade, the money will circulate through every part of the nation and increase the demand for the products both of the farm and the factory.

The building of these works—extending as they must over a number of years—will not only prevent unemployment during the period of building but the wealth they will create and liberate when done will step up the whole country to a new level of prosperity. For they will not only add directly to production by the provision of power but they will still further spread out industry which will in turn stimulate other lines of activity and thus increase the employment opportunities of the people.

An element that serves to delay the beginning of these great public projects is the belief that public resources should be retained by the government and also operated by the government. Behind this belief is the thought that ownership is more important than use, and it begets a condition wherein the people have to pay an exorbitant public cost instead of a reasonable private profit.

For it is a demonstrated fact that private ownership can earn a satisfactory profit in any form of enterprise, charging prices or rates which under government operation would result in a loss. I have never heard of a man who has had any experience at all in the conduct of any kind of business who believes in government ownership or operation. It is wasteful and it is bound to be wasteful because men working under the government and subject to inexpert direction, and political indecision, and frequent partisan investigations, not to speak of the vagaries of theoretical reformers who think that business is the enemy from which the people must be saved are more interested in avoiding the doing of anything that might be criticized than in getting ahead. Indeed—regardless of salary—it is almost out of the question for a government to engage the best managerial brains. The best brains will always care more for the work than for the job, but in the government the temptation is to retain the job.

All this is true wherever the government has sought to enter business. I must say, however, that in the government's proper business there has usually been a fortunate amount of brains. It is the brains in government that realize best the hopelessness of a government becoming a business success in any sense. There is no profit and loss account staring a government in the face. There is no check upon high prices or poor service, such as customers can exercise upon private concerns. A government can monopolize a service and thus compel one to use it, it can under-serve and over-charge and make one pay a deficit in the form of taxes. All these conditions are utterly destructive of all the elements of business.

As to the possibility of a private profit when the resources of the nation, such as water power, are developed, to my mind the logical approach is this: Which is the more important: What the man gets? Or what the public gets? What we lose sight of is the fact that every development of whatever kind is a public development. Nothing other than wide and satisfactory public use can make any private venture profitable. The public, in the last resort, has the full use of every private service, with none of the responsibilities should it prove a loss or a failure. But under government ownership the deficits come out of the public pocket in taxes. Private profits go back to the public. There is nothing else to do with them. No man can spend much on himself or his family, and his surplus has to go back into some enterprise from which he hopes to gain a profit.

All of this does not mean that the government should have no part. But the great duty of the government in public and other works is to make the way easy for the public to gain benefits. It is not equipped to make prosperity, but it is equipped to make prosperity possible— just as it is equipped to make prosperity impossible.

The chief danger here is that a programme of development may be so twisted as to become a programme of charity—that work will be allotted to men because they need jobs and not because the work ought to be done.

The very best charity is to help a man to a place where he will never need charity. Nothing seems more useless than the trouble we take to ease the effects, when half that trouble would serve to destroy the cause.

Human sympathy is a great motive power, and no cool, calculating attitude will take the place of it. All great advances are due to human sympathy. But we have been using this great motive force for too small ends. If human sympathy prompts us to feed the hungry, why should it not give a much greater prompting toward making hunger impossible? If we have sympathy enough for people to help them in their trouble, surely we ought to have feeling enough to help them out of their trouble. It is a curious fact that more people can be got to help relieve poverty than can be got to devote their energies to removing poverty altogether.

Our first duty we owe to ourselves. We must do our best where we are. We must be fair where we are. We must do honest work where we are. No one who throws down his tools is helping to abolish poverty. Whatever we do in the future we may be sure of this: We shall never be able to make any programme go without work.

Work is a good quality to be developed. Every man who works is helping to drive poverty out of the world —first his own and then that of his fellow beings.

The man who does better and more productive work to-day than he did yesterday is a social reformer of the highest type. It is not the men who are doing the talking that are solving our problems, but the men who are at work.

Every age teems with theories which need only to stand a while before their falsity will be revealed. If a thing is right it will endure. If it is wrong, the public mind simply outgrows it. No one can imagine how much worse off we should be if we followed every theory and every leader that promised us a golden age. So if our progress seems slow it is only because of the people's carefulness not to make a misstep. But there is progress being made all the time, now in this direction, now in that, and then all along the line.

One very great false move would be to make charity a substitute for reform. We can give by developing. We cannot develop by giving.

CHAPTER IX

THE NEW CRAFTSMANSHIP

THE notion is dying that a machine-made article cannot be so fine as one made by hand; but it seems to be still taken for granted that the operator of a machine is not so skilled and resourceful a craftsman as the old hand worker, that the general level of mechanical skill is lowering and that machine products will by their uniformity result in a dull, ugly sort of world. People who live in books uniformly take that view of things.

This view is not important, but it is important that we separate the facts from the fancies, for not without machinery can the more important economic problems of the world be solved. The consequences of misleading the world on this point—which is hardly possible for long—could easily become tragic.

Take first the effect of machine operating upon men. It has been so often asserted as to be commonplace that the almost mechanical tending of a machine takes away not only a man's skill but also his initiative and makes him into some sort of a strange creature that looks like a man but really is not a man. The error here is in assuming that all machines are alike, that all of them require only mechanical attendance and that the men operating them are highly skilled machinists wasting their lives away.

All machines are far from being alike and their operations call for various kinds of intellects and perceptions. If a machine requires no judgment at all to operate, then it is better to make it automatic than bother a man to attend it. The lowest order of men who are now operating machinery with us are the men who a few years ago would have been classed as unskilled labour, and would have been compelled to eke out miserable existences as draught animals with hods or wheel barrows or in back-breaking tasks with picks, shovels, and crowbars. As we have learned more about economical manufacturing we have steadily cut out the jobs requiring brute strength and also we have cut out the jobs that required little or no intelligence—though we have never had a job of any kind for the unskilled man which did not require more acute perceptions than the rough jobs to which he had been accustomed as an unskilled labourer. Formerly we had a certain number of jobs which required very little mental effort on the part of the worker or attendant; we found that the men who stayed in those jobs were the men who did not want to exert their minds or who had very little in the way of minds to exert. It would be most unfortunate if industry provided places only for the thinking men. For then the unthinking would become public charges—the very poor are recruited almost solely from the people who refuse to think and therefore refuse to work diligently.

We still have some jobs which require no special ability to fill and these jobs are occupied by men earning at least seven dollars a day who would otherwise be able to pick up only odd jobs of heavy work. No intelligent man could or would stay in these jobs—and we would not permit an intelligent man to stay in one. The work done in them is monotonous in the extreme but invariably they are filled with the kind of men who welcome monotony because it does not call for thought. And yet even in these jobs some skill is needed.

Possibly the requirement is not for skill but for a higher alertness than is necessary in, say, a ditch digger or a crossing tender. The man has to know what he is doing—no matter how mechanical the task—or he will fall behind in his work and also he will continue to operate when something goes wrong. The call is for something in the nature of craftsmanship but of a kind different from what is usually comprehended in that word. No matter what mechanical precautions are taken against human error, a man without what might be called machine sense will spoil much work if allowed to go on. At least some grade of intuition is required for even the lowest job. It takes a higher grade of man to manage an electric hoist than to manage a plain block and tackle. The lowest job in our factory to-day requires a higher grade of intelligence than the lowest job in the best hand factory of the older days. This is a fact of which those who praise the good old days are not aware. Craftsmen one hundred years ago were not comparatively so numerous as they are now. Only a few names have come down to us. To-day, high-grade craftsmanship is the commonplace of industry. It has to be.

It is usually assumed that in the old machine shop

all the men were highly skilled journeymen or apprentices on the way to becoming skilled. That was never the case. Even in the best shops the proportion of first-class machinists was very small and a fair part of the work was always done by semi-skilled or unskilled labourers who were mostly hired for their strength. To-day not only is the lowest job in our industries much higher than the lowest job in the old industrial set-up, but also the highest jobs call for more skill and craftsmanship than few, if any, of the older craftsmen possessed. We have in our industries no absolutely unskilled men but, taking our lowest grade as comparable with the old unskilled, then the proportion of highly skilled men to unskilled is higher to-day than ever it was. And judging from our own experience this stepping-up process will continue. We to-day employ a higher proportion of skilled machinists than ever we employed and every development that we make calls for more such men. This will not be so extraordinary as at first it seems if only one looks over what has happened in the last twenty-five years of machine production.

The earlier machines had such a limited field of work that the designers of products were also limited to crude essentials. To-day machines are so much more capable than they used to be that the designers of work and products are not limited. The tradition of hand work is a serious hindrance to the minds of designers. Designs which will take more advantage of the power of machines to go beyond what hand work can do will give us a whole new art. There are some signs of this already.

Skill and originality did not die with the hand-made age. A craftsman has been defined as "an artisan, some-

times an artist," and the definition of an artist is: "One
who professes and practises an art in which imagination
and taste preside over the execution, especially a fine art,
as painting or sculpture." Further he is defined as "one
who shows trained skill or rare taste in any art or occupa-
tion." This last phrase hits the mark. The old-time craftsman only occasionally showed trained skill. Very few
became masters. More frequently their skill was primitive
and their tastes poor. Some collectors see the merit of
antiques in the fact that they were hand-made—no matter
how crudely. But seldom were they literally hand-made.
From the most remote times the potter had his wheel
and the weaver his loom. Both were machines. The great
change has been in the motive power that drives them.
Anciently it was hand power, foot power, wind, or water
power; now it is steam or electricity, but wind and water
are still basic elements in the production of mechanical
energy.

Once the word "machine" had a much broader signifi-
cance than it has to-day. It was commonly applied to a
coach, a cart, a ship, or a boat. The term "engine" was
applied to devices for carrying on war, as well as con-
trivances used in peaceful occupations. What has happened through the centuries is that more and more
machinery has been invented and more effective means of
driving it have been discovered.

The industrialist of the present day cannot discard the
means he possesses of producing things quickly, accurately, and effectively for the purpose of going back to
less efficient methods. As the needs of mankind have grown
the means of production have had to be increased and

improved. The use of machinery in making things is not new.

At Dearborn we have gathered specimens of nearly all the articles that have been used in this country since its settling, with the thought of assembling them so that anyone who cares to discover what the people of any past generation commonly used in their daily lives will have only to go to the proper wing of the museum that we are building and there see every household article, every kind of vehicle, every sort of tool. One may review the common household articles from the handicraft stage, through the hand and machine stage, to the machine stage, and then through the progress of machine work.

The hand-made articles are on the whole better than the first machine articles and are certainly better looking; the first machine articles tried to be like the hand-made instead of striking out for themselves. But the later machine articles are much finer than the average hand-made. It is to be remembered, however, that the examples of fine workmanship that have come down to us from former periods are only the very best specimens and are not at all representative of what people in general used. A finely made article of any kind represented a long period of hand labour. That labour was ill paid, but so much of it had to be used that the resulting article was very expensive and therefore its ownership was restricted to the wealthy.

The arts of the old craftsman have not been lost and neither have his materials. If we do not follow him in our work of to-day, it is not because we cannot, but because in every respect we have improved mightily on what he did. We can, if we so care, do anything that he did and do it better. This has been conclusively proven to me by our experiences in the repair of the specimens which we have collected. Each specimen will eventually be restored to the exact condition in which it was originally used and already we have restored so many thousands of articles as to have called on every variety of crafts-manship—yet there has never yet been a job of any kind which someone taken right out of the rank and file of our workers could not do. In round figures, we employ about one hundred thousand men in the Detroit district. This would have been the trades-working army of a fair-sized state in the older days, because then the agricultural popu-lation was always much larger than the industrial, but I greatly doubt whether any country containing two million people—which would have been about the population to have a hundred thousand artisans—could have mustered such an army of skill as we find in our plants. If we want to restore an old house or an old inn, we have no trouble in locating carpenters among our forces who can take exactly the same sort of tools that the old carpenters used and turn out just as good work as they did. It is likewise with cabinet making and we have some of the finest examples of cabinet making that the old craftsmen ever created. In metal working we repair without difficulty every possible sort of machine or instrument from the most delicate watches and scientific instruments to steam engines and locomotives. Most of these articles are un-familiar to our men and so first of all they have to find out how they originally worked. That in itself requires a high grade of mechanical intelligence. Then they must

take the thing apart, clean and polish every part, and
finally rebuild—replacing worn, broken, or missing parts.
This calls for a very wide range of skill and ingenuity,
yet not in a single instance have our men been stumped.
They have been able not only to make any required part
but to make it better and more accurately than the original
part. They can do this very quickly with modern tools
but when, just as an experiment, we require them to use
only the tools that the old workers had, they manage just
as well as did the old worker. And when I say that they
use the old tools, I mean just that, for we have thousands
of specimens of old tools restored to their original condition and we are able to fit out a worker with a kit of
any period.

As far as materials are concerned, we to-day have at
our command such a variety of metals and alloys that
we are always able to supply a very much better material
for a part than that which was originally used. But if
necessary we can make the exact grade of iron, steel,
brass, or copper that the first worker had.

There is nothing at all to the legend that the ancients
had materials which we cannot duplicate or which were
better than anything we now know. Every engineer and
metallurgist knows that. Indeed, if we had not progressed
in the metals, many of our modern conveniences—including the automobile—would be impossible, for our machines
would be so heavy and clumsy as to be impractical. It
is impossible to say whether the best workers of former
years, given the tools of to-day, would be as skilled as
the men of to-day, but it is possible to say with absolute
certainty and from the facts that the best craftsmen of

the older days had no more ability than the best craftsmen of to-day and that the grade of workmanship of
to-day with the use of machine tools is higher than anything which was previously possible.

The progress which has already been made seems
scarcely to have been comprehended. For instance, automobile manufacturers to-day turn out as a matter of
course an engine which is more precisely made than the
finest watch. This is literally true not only for measurements but also for balance. Very few watches are made
to a thousandths of an inch, but that accuracy is quite
commonplace in automobile parts of considerable weight.
The revolving parts of an engine such as the crankshaft
and the flywheel are brought to a balance, both dynamic
and static, approximating that of the balance wheel of a
fine watch. This does not mean that accuracy has just
been discovered or anything of the sort. The real point
is that the accuracy which was once reserved for the
most expensive instruments is now available for the affairs
of everyday life.

The accurate making of common utilities means far
more than is at first apparent. The machinery of to-day,
especially that which is used in general life away from
the machine shop, has to have its parts absolutely interchangeable so that it can be repaired by a non-skilled man
and also in order that freight and carriage may be saved
by assembling the machine at the point where it is to be
used. A practical interchangeability can be obtained
without extreme accuracy and the requirements of interchangeability have long since been met. There is a further
and higher requirement. The unnecessary vibration of

any moving part represents a waste in the transmitting of power and also a waste in the unnecessary wear and tear. The campaign against noise is in some of its phases a campaign against lost motion—that is, against waste. The vibration of machinery may be due to many causes but generally it is traceable to lack of balance and inaccurate fitting. Therefore making machines accurately is one of the best-known ways of cheapening them. As we cut down the vibration we not only conserve power but also increase the life of the machine and therefore make its operation less expensive.

There is nothing new about this. The trouble has been to devise ways and means of attaining accuracy without at the same time so adding to the cost of production as to make the price of the machine beyond the purses of more than a few of the people. It has always been possible to attain accuracy but not to attain both accuracy and complete interchangeability at a low cost. The economic effects of accuracy are a study all of themselves.

The attaining of accuracy at a low cost is a very gradual process that does not come to any industry in a day. One of the very great advantages of a factory turning out only a single product is the opportunity that is given for the detailed study of the manufacturing of each part. We have discovered that, no matter how carefully we plan a method of making, experience always shows us a better way. That can be taken as a universal principle. The general trend in our own work of late years has been away from the intricate subdividing of operations and toward the combining of them. In the earlier days of hand craftsmanship a single worker did all of a job; then came

the cruder machinery and it was found most economical
to split up the operations so that each machine and each
man did just one small thing. Now we are heading back
to the old days except that where then one man did the
whole of a job, now a machine as far as possible does all
of a job. The ideal would be a completely automatic machine operating to whatever degree of accuracy might be
required. That ideal, however, is very far from being
realized except with rather simple parts. The best that
we can do is to combine as many operations as possible,
using to a very considerable extent the principle of the
turret lathe—which is one of the most important principles in modern manufacturing. For example, if a part
had to be drilled, bored, reamed, turned, and faced under
the old system it would pass through eight or nine single-
purpose machines each managed by a man and there
would be a great deal of handling and of opportunity for
error. Now most of these operations are performed on a
single machine with a single operator who just clamps the
part into a turret. At a given time, based on the number
of minutes required for the job, the forging is released
from the first operation and whirled along to the second
station, which may be the drilling. Meanwhile, another
rough forging has been loaded and revolved from the
loading point to the first station. From the second station
the forging goes on to a third, where remachining may
be done automatically; then to a fourth, where it may
be finished.

On one of these multi-spindle or turret machines there
are usually from five to seven stations in addition to the
loading point. They are arranged in a circle so that the

forging, after it has been machined at the different points as required, will complete the circle, returning to the operator as a finished part. He removes it and places it on a conveyor, at the same time taking from the conveyor a rough forging, which is inserted in the chuck left vacant by the removal of the finished part.

Thus there is no lost time or motion; the parts are handled but twice—once in loading as a rough forging and again in removing as a finished part. The machines turn out, in a comparatively few minutes, parts which under the old system would have required hours or even days to build. The handling of parts has been cut down in many cases to two or three operations. Some parts are reduced in cost more than one half and the degree of accuracy more than doubled.

Under the hand methods of production, the final operations were cutting and trying—nothing ever quite fitted and if an exact fitting were required, the part had to be ground into place. In our method of production and in modern American methods generally, inspection takes the place of the old cutting and trying and some of the most ingenious machinery used anywhere is that devised to reduce the human factor in inspection. No matter how accurately production machinery may be adjusted, no two parts turned out by the same machine will ever be exactly alike—the material itself never runs with precise uniformity. It is the function of inspection not merely to discover defects but to make certain that each part is of the size, weight, and balance required. Some of this inspecting is highly delicate and quite beyond anything in the range of unaided human perception. What would ordinarily be a complex laboratory test has to be simplified to a point where the same results as in the laboratory can be had in the shop as a matter of routine.

The engine crankshaft is an example. A crankshaft has to be a strong but at the same time a very exact piece of work. And it has to be balanced dynamically, which means while running. The balancing machine resembles a table and rests on spring pivots so that it will oscillate whenever a steady vibration is set up. The shaft is placed on this table, supported by bearings, and is secured at the gear end to a flywheel similar to that on the car itself.

Next the angle of unbalance is determined by another rotating operation on the same machine. By using a simple chart the operator translates the figures given by his instrument into a definite direction regarding the angle at which to drill and the number and depth of the holes needed to balance the shaft. After one end of the shaft has been tested it goes to the drilling operation for the required amount to be removed to bring it in dynamic balance. When the one end has been dynamically balanced and checked the other is brought to a similar balance by a much simpler process. By means of an instrument developed by our men, they can detect the out-of-balance of the other end by balancing it statically.

The directions for correcting the out-of-balance are chalked on each crankshaft by the chart operator. The crankshaft then goes to a drill operator who places it in a fixture on the table of his machine. By means of a locating pin every shaft placed there must take a position identical with that which it occupied on the balancing machine. There is a drill at each end of the table, placed directly over the end cheek of the shaft. Each drill is equipped with a disk that, revolving as the drill is pressed down, registers exactly the depth in thousandths to which it has gone. This eliminates any chance of taking off too much or too little weight to balance the crankshaft.

These examples are selected only to show something of the delicate coördination of large-scale American industry. There are no rough-and-ready operations. We use tremendous quantities of brute strength but none of it comes from human beings—it comes through electric wires. The men who work with these machines need to have a certain amount of manual dexterity but above all they need such a coördination of their faculties that they can adjust themselves to the tempo of production. The man does not become a machine, for he must above all be keen and alert. He has to comprehend the importance of little things and when, a few years ago, we made sweeping changes in our methods of manufacturing and greatly raised the standards of accuracy, one of the largest obstacles that we met was the refusal of men to adjust themselves to the new standards. We had to change a very considerable portion of our personnel simply because so many of the older men stubbornly refused to believe that the new standards of accuracy could be attained.

Although a machine may be nearly automatic and the part which the attendant plays would not seem to be important, we have discovered that only highly intelligent men can sufficiently comprehend what their machines are doing and unless they do comprehend they will not properly attend their work. A few years ago we had no production job which could not be learned by any man of average intelligence within a month and perhaps one half of our jobs could be learned in a week. To-day the proportion of jobs which can be learned in a week or less is rather small and to learn any of the more important production tasks requires a training of from two weeks to a month—provided the man has some native mechanical ability. The more delicate jobs of inspecting and balancing require from six to eight weeks to learn and a slow-witted man can never learn them. These are only jobs in production—that is, in making parts which are eventually assembled into an automobile.

The keeping of the vast quantities of machinery in repair, the providing of dies and tools and the nice adjustment of everything, it will easily be realized, require a multitude of machinists who are master craftsmen. The uninformed seem to imagine that machines are just built and that thenceforth they operate without human aid. That, of course, is absurd. Modern industry demands more highly skilled men and more of them than are in the world to-day. We are distinctly short of skilled men and one of the weaknesses of industry is that in general it has not been able to provide the facilities for training the army of men that are now needed. Our company is doing what it can to meet this shortage by the intensive training of likely young men and the promoting to the more technical jobs of the more intelligent men in production. But unless the pace of industry slackens it is going to continue to be short of skilled men. The situation is exactly the reverse of what it is commonly supposed to be, for, instead of industry requiring a constantly lessening proportion of skilled men, it is requiring a constantly growing proportion. These men require not only skill but also versatility—and it is harder to get versatility than it is to get skill. On the whole, however, among the many admirable qualities of the men who work for wages in this country not the least admirable is their adaptiveness. For instance, the passing of coal mining is a tragedy in England and would also be a tragedy in this country had not other industrial opportunities opened to our miners. The American miner does not make a lifework of it, anyway. It satisfies his sense of adventure in young manhood, and then he finds other work. The American workingman can turn his hand to anything. If he goes out of business as a blacksmith he opens a garage. If mining fails him he goes in for building or some other trade.

But I cannot regard it as an inherent weakness of industry that once a man is employed he is not then forever employed in the same factory. If a man be misplaced in an industry, the sooner he discovers it or the sooner his employer discovers it, then the better off is that man. We have in our industries jobs for every grade of ability and every grade of physique, but we have no jobs at all for the man who is interested only in getting whatever money he can out of us. Any industry which would set itself— or be compelled to set itself—to take care of this class of man is contributing to economic waste. Perhaps it is wrong to say "this class of man." It is inconceivable that a man can exist who cannot gain an interest in some kind of job somewhere. That, however, is a point that I have previously touched on.

The men themselves are beginning to realize that industry is not what it has seemed to be, and that many of its distortions are only growing pains. One of our company publications held a letter-writing competition in order to find out how many of our men were interested enough to write a letter, and also to gain something of their views. Here is a letter from a blacksmith which is valuable from a number of angles. First, it gives the reaction of a craftsman to machine industry; and second, it shows something of the level of workers' intelligence.

Being a trained blacksmith, I naturally take most of my impressions of my work from the angle of the way they affect my craft. Since I started to work in the drop forge department, I cannot help realizing how the almost miraculous efficiency of the system is daily rendering what is perhaps the most ancient handicraft as obsolete as the advance of the automobile has made the old methods of road transportation. It is almost uncanny to see, for the first time, a hammerman, with merely a few blows from a steam hammer, forge a perfectly shaped crankshaft, or other part, which then needs only one operation of a trimming press to make it a job which a highly skilled blacksmith would take several working days to emulate.

If I was amazed when I started to work in the forge department, how can I hope to express my feeling at the wonderful improvement in production methods? The heating of the steel stock is perhaps the best illustration of my point. The method in use when I was hired was to put twenty-five bars in the furnace at one time; then they were heated and forged and another lot put into the furnace, so there was always some time lost between "heats." But thought was applied to this business, and now the bars travel along rails through a regulated furnace which needs only one man to load, and the rest is done by an electrically operated automatic pusher. Thus there is a constant stream of correctly heated bars continually being supplied to the hammermen with a minimum of labour expended in the operation.

Undoubtedly the great lesson I have learned from my work is that we are really only entering the age of machinery and that our system of production must inevitably become the standard system. There can be no question that while the methods being used are getting better results, with machinelike precision and at an almost incalculable saving of time than did the old methods, progress is still advancing in industry.

The machine is the greatest and most versatile of all broadening powers. That will soon be grasped.

In the ordinary course of things, hand and brain must work together to accomplish any results; to divorce one from the other would be like depriving a ship of its navigator and allowing it to run wheresoever it listed. The result would be disaster. This combination of hand and brain is essential to success. The farmer prepares the soil and sows the seed, but even with the most propitious weather conditions the cultivation of the land and the planting of the seed would lead to poor results were it not for judicious selection and proper fertilization.

It is the same in the work of the engineer and builder. A steel girder may be a perfect piece of workmanship, but it takes the guiding hand of the engineer to place it where it belongs; a pier or a buttress may be a marvel of strength, but it is the architect who decides its position so that it may give strength where most required. Both engineer and architect have made a study of these things and their judgment is relied upon.

The man who uses his brains as well as his hands in the performance of a given task, or the man whose intelligence fits him for the guidance and direction of others in the carrying out of his work, is as much a working man as any. He is just as truly a man who works. And so it is in any profession. All who perform their duty faithfully

K.

are working men in as true a sense as the toiler in the woods, the fields, or the factory. All who are engaged in legitimate labour, be it with the hands or with the brains, are working men; all who are not idle have the right to be included in this designation.

CHAPTER X

MANAGEMENT AND SIZE

A FIXED and rigid system of management is not really a system of management at all—it is just a system. And anyone who attempts to manage according to rules will do well to inquire whether he is managing or is being managed. For the nice point in management is to discover whether one is directing affairs or whether one is being directed by them.

It is quite easy to sit in an office, read reports, and know more or less about everything—after it has happened. But that is not management. Everything that happens or can happen in—that is, within, inside—a business ought to be the direct result of what the managers have specifically arranged. If these results are good it will be because the judgment of the managers has been good. The complete responsibility for success or for failure is with the management. But when I say "the management" I mean managers—men; I do not mean a system of precedents and by-laws.

The sea captain sails by his charts; he can do that because the sea route has been charted. But American business is now sailing over seas that have never been passed before. There are no management charts in the wheelhouse of progressive business; if there are, they are the charts of areas long past. What American business is depending

on now is the man on the bridge—the living manager—
whose only charts are his foresight and his insight and his
sense of the new trade winds that are beginning to blow.
To suggest that one can make a manager by stuffing him
full of a system of management which worked fairly well
ten or twenty years ago is to suggest that business is a
ferry boat plying in familiar waters between two commonplace ports. But business to-day is an explorer's ship;
it is always meeting new conditions; no system of management can guide it: it depends on the man on the bridge.
If we can only get clearly in mind the difference between
a system of management and a manager, then we shall
have come a long step toward facing present business
problems from the angle of mastery.

Sometimes we of the Ford Motor Company meet men
who have taken our books as their business Bibles and
are trying to run their businesses as we ran ours ten years
ago. They thought they had found in our books a complete
system of management which only needed to be applied
and it would automatically produce results. But what the
books recorded was the result of substituting the vital
manager-mind for the dead management-mind. If there
was any value in this it was in the suggestion that the man
and not the system should always dominate. Of what use
was it, then, for any business man to take our results and
create another system of management out of them? What
we want him to do is to disregard all systems, get to the
wheel of his own business, and give himself to it. That is
the only effective management to-day—the vital cord of
connection between the man and the service he is trying
to give society through his business.

Of course, this is not a theory of management. It is a theory of business. And doubtless the old wrong theory of management has persisted so long because the old lazy and selfish theory of business has persisted so long. Business has been regarded as a pump which can be profitably used to supply the needs of the owners of the pump. If the pump could be made to operate automatically and thus relieve its owners from the labour of operating the pump handle, so much the better; it would be regarded as a great advance in business method. In reality it would be a great reverse. Systems of management are designed to relieve owners from running their own pumps. The owners desire to be thus relieved because they do not see that their pumps are necessary to social salvation—that is, they do not see business in other than a narrowly selfish light. Now, if the mutations of past business experience and the omens of the immediate future are saying anything to us, it is that business is more than a means of providing its owners with a living and luxuries, that business is national defense and social education and economic supply and racial destiny all rolled into one, that it is this day our one earthly anchor to all that civilization means, and that the business man is nothing more than a dollar-a-year man serving in a great cause. We saw that during the war. Why is it that we do not see it in this greater present crisis? Without noise of machinery, without operation of political laws, even without the knowledge of the prophets and wise men of the selfish order or system, business is shifting its base —rather, is being shifted. The gap between what the traffic will bear and fair and equal exchange of goods and services grows wider. The system of what the traffic

will bear is doomed, has heard its doom, and is moving
away into outer darkness. Nothing seemed so solid and
stable as the edifice of selfish business: in reality it is this
moment as a snow bank slowly settling under the April
sun. It is disappearing in response to a law that Congress
would not recognize even if it walked right down the
centre aisle to the Speaker's desk.

If this is true, and probably no man high enough in the
watch tower of business to see all round could be found to
deny it, what does it say to the younger business man
about management? It says simply this: If business is
your call, your service, your contribution to your kind,
treat it as such. Never regard it as a pump that may be
automatically operated to fetch you personal profits. Regard it as part of the vital social organism on which all
life values depend. And beware of the ways and means
used in the old selfish systems of business. These are of
no more use to us now than the racks and torture systems
of the past. This is a new time. You yourself must take
control of your business. It must be your work, your
pleasure, your profession, your gain, and your loss—this
service of business in which you are engaged: your art,
your science, your religion; for business is all these. And
when it becomes even approximately any of these, what
do you see? You see a man who is a manager, and not a
man who is the operator of some system of management.
And you see a business that is alive not only commer-
cially, but along every avenue of life. This is not only coming: it is already here. The men on the bridge of business
will confirm this.

There is nothing that will contribute to making a proper

conception of management so much as a proper conception of the function of business: and without a proper view of business, no management, however energetic and alert it may be, can achieve success. Business success is not measured by what owners may be able to gather for themselves, but by what the business does to the country. By this standard of judgment, business has left us much to desire. It has not been wholly successful. No activity that periodically lets down a nation, or that repeatedly commits the same error at the public expense, can be called successful. If the founders of our government had so constructed it that at periods of five or ten years the governmental system should collapse, we would be quick to conclude that they had not been successful builders of government, that the design they built upon was wrong, or that the managers were incapable. Shall we be less intelligently critical or outspoken regarding business? The degree to which business is intelligent and responsible may be determined by the degree of shame and better resolution with which it views its failure to function to the comfort and security of the whole people. Whatever breaks down shows wrong design or poor management. Business, however exalted by financial power and commercial prowess, cannot be made an exception to this rule.

And yet it would be wrong to conclude that the betterment we seek is to be found in abstracting something from business as it now exists. I cannot see in any productive and serviceable business a single element that ought to be removed. The direction in which we have been moving seems to be the right one. What we have been doing seems to be necessary and useful. We are not confronted with the task of tearing down and throwing away what we have built. What is needed is rather the *addition* of something which is now lacking, the *addition of a new ingredient* more representative of the human personality which is, after all, the mainspring of business. The damage wrought by neatly carpentered systems of management is that they have permitted a divided personality. A man was a business man for the purpose of gaining enough money to permit him to be something else. Now, an artist is not an artist for the purpose of gaining enough means and leisure to become a brickmason, nor is a statesman devoted to statecraft for the purpose of finding means to raise horses. But business as a makeshift and not as a career in the public service has been quite widely practiced. All systems of management are in the interests of those who would get as far away from their business as possible and run it by proxy. No man devoted to his science or art or other service runs it by proxy. Deprived of the whole personality, business has been crippled. It has developed such pathological slogans as "business is business." As a matter of fact, business is human. Nothing human is alien to it. That is the missing ingredient. When it is added the whole character of the mixture is changed.

It is during fair weather that management needs to be especially alert and wary. There is nothing so trying to the morale of a business organization as a run of success. The tendency then is to let the business run on and fill its orders while the leaders pleasantly contemplate their triumph. The danger is not apparent, but it is already present. It is the same danger that assails the football squad after the training and playing season is over: the organiza-

tion goes soft. The wise manager will be oftener on his
rounds in so-called good times because it is in good times
that all the seeds of bad times are sown. That is a fact
impressed upon the business community ceaselessly, but
so far it has not been accepted. In times of good business the wise manager will keep his organization in as
strict training as when the outside going is harder. He
will reduce the price, perhaps; not for the purpose of increasing sales (that is seldom the really important result)
but for the purpose of keeping his organization keen on
the quest of better methods. He will deliberately project
into a satisfactory market an improved article, not because
the public is demanding it (the public seldom does) but
because he knows that he cannot afford to let his organization slump. The health of that creative, productive organization is more to him than any of the lesser concerns such
as the stock market or the fireworks of speculative mer-
chandising. Like the captain, the wise manager keeps that
ship—that organization—first in his mind. Fair weather
is no idling time for him. In business, as a matter of fact,
fair weather is the time when all the leaks are made. Every
period of so-called prosperity is a new opportunity to
study the ways in which unwise management goes about
to help create a period of so-called depression.

Take the last period of prosperity as an example.
What did it do to American business? The worst thing it
did was to take the brains out of business. Business men
in larger numbers than ever before deserted the altars of
service and worshipped at the altars of Mammon. I mean
they quit making goods and went to making money. A
man's heart is where his treasure is, and multitudes of

business men had their treasure on the market. Their real business, for the time, was playing the stocks. Their businesses ran on, after a fashion. But, so far as the health of any business is concerned, it makes no difference whether its master's mania is the race track or the stock market, the business suffers from the lack of his whole interest.

Most of these men are back at work now, but some of them will never be as good workers again. The taste of speculative gain has weakened their creative fibre. Some, however, have learned a lesson not only of value of themselves but of great value to the country: when next we have a period called prosperity these men will be preventing the causes of reversal. One is very hopeful over American business when one sees the willingness of business men to learn a lesson. The business fabric of America, and by that I mean the intellectual and moral calibre of our business men, is far stronger to-day than it was two years ago. Business men have learned that there is no substitute for work and that there is no gain comparable to mastery of their craft.

The objective of every business must be the doing of a useful thing in the most economical manner. No business will run itself. No methods or formulas can be devised to substitute for human judgment and leadership. There can be no judgment without a complete knowledge of that which is to be judged. There can be no leadership if the leader does not know what he is leading. The leadership must be in one person, and therefore the final and decisive judgment must be in one person.

Business holds no place for democracy, if by democracy

is meant the shaping of policies by the vote of a large number of people or their delegates. The theory of democratic government as applied to a nation has never proved sufficiently practical even to be tried. This is because the theory makes no provision at all for getting anything done. It starts and it stops with discussion. That which is usually called democracy boils down to the ability of a leader to convince a majority of all the people that what he has done or is doing is right and for their best interests.

An industrial organization has to be formed for a purpose, and the quality of its performance does not have to be guessed at or argued about. The balance sheet gives the results. No corporation can continue over a period of years to have income exceed outgo otherwise than by performing a service. It may for a time violate the service principles which are inherent in business, but not for very long. The application of the principles is a matter both of judgment and of leadership.

It does not do the head of a business any good simply to have the information or to have so much of it thrust upon him that he has no time to exercise judgment. The vital things in a business ought to be known day by day so that any necessary correctives may be applied at once. The correctives may not be applied at once; sometimes it helps in the training of men to let the horse be stolen— provided one watches the stealing and can recover the animal in due season. This is another sign of wise management—sometimes permitting a condition to grow worse in order to disclose further weaknesses in an organization and also to reveal those persons who are sensitive to the condition existing. To be everlastingly tinkering at small defects may be a waste of the attention and energy necessary to the bigger task. The use of wrong trends as a revealer of further wrongs may be very effective in the hands of a wise manager, but, of course, it is next to impossible under any form of stock management. The main fact is that the management must centralize with the men who know what is going on.

Therefore, democracy in business is not a desirable ideal, if it be taken to mean that policies are to be shaped by the votes of a large number of people, none of whom can know all that is going on. My conception of democracy in management has to do with the recognition of ability and with clearing the way for the advancement of each man according to his capacity. For then we can be reasonably certain that things will be done by those who are best able to do them, and that each man will be rewarded according to his merit as a doer and not as a speaker. No one can persuade an automobile to run just by talking to it. Yet it is that rather than the recognition of merit and accomplishment which seems to be behind the democratic ideal as applied to industry.

I believe that true management begins with the product and its making, and that into them must go the largest measure of leadership, for the pressure to better both the product and its method of manufacturing must be continuous. One can never be satisfied. Pressing for improvement and repelling self-satisfaction require leadership. Finance then becomes simply a part of the schedule of production. We need certain supplies of a specified quality at certain places at certain times. That is a matter of planning. We need certain amounts of money to pay the men, to pay for the supplies, and to pay for additions or changes in equipment. That is a matter of planning. But this money is merely an inevitable result of correct operating.

We find a way to perform each operation, and the results of these operations assemble into our product. All that remains is to see that our instructions are everywhere carried out. The human tendency is to depart from instructions. Therefore the duty of that part of the management which is not primarily involved in design is to see that the designs are followed. The head of a department is responsible for that department—responsible for seeing that the plans, as they concern his department, are absolutely followed. And on down the line each superintendent and foreman is charged with seeing that the plans are followed in his sector.

A given amount of material should result in a definite output and employ a definite number of men. The standards, through practice and improvements in methods, should constantly become better. If instead they become worse, then that is something to be looked after. Thus it is possible to keep one's finger always on the pulse of the business without taking one's attention away from the really important matter of improving the business.

Of course we have other checks. We have a squad at the Dearborn laboratory whose sole duty is to go out through the shops, take anything they see, and fetch it to Dearborn for testing. Our business will not run properly unless everything down to the minutest detail is done exactly according to plan and schedule, and, although at every stage of production every conceivable test and inspection is made, we maintain this flying squadron as an additional and independent check. And the flying squadron itself every once in a while has to be checked.

Under our method of management, with everything thought out in advance and everything converging to a single product, the size of our institution does not matter. In fact, the larger we become the more cheaply we can manufacture, for then we can use bigger and faster tools. In many ways it would be simpler to make a million cars a day than to make a thousand, for in a thousand the very best methods of manufacturing might require equipment which would not be warranted by the volume of the output. Size of plant is of no matter if the thing produced be for the benefit of the public and sold at as low a price as possible.

Our method of management is founded on the assumption that the whole corporation is just a tool for doing one thing. The size of a tool is determined by the kind of work that is to be done and by its facility. That is, one would not use a crowbar on a watch, nor would one put a ten-ton shovel in the hands of a ditch digger. The question of size often arises with reference to management. Questions are asked, How large is too large? How large may a plant be without exceeding the possibilities of efficient management? And the answer is always the same: Few businesses can grow too large; all healthy businesses are growing larger; the attempt to measure the possible extent of management by geographical limits is an error. We do not know as yet where the limits of efficient management are. We do know that some forms of business do not lend themselves to large expansion under single management. They are too personal in their service or too local in their adaptation to be national. Taken together they comprise very large businesses, but the need of local management cannot be met except by local management. But industrially it is possible to say that management is coextensive with the control of design. Control the design of the product and the method of its production, and the same results can be obtained in one plant or a hundred, in America or in Europe, for one year or ten. It is, when all is said and done, the work that exercises the control.

There is passive and there is active management. The first merely observes what is done, but the second really manages. A positive centralized control which always presses for better designs and better methods of making is the only real management. It is not managing merely to sit and watch things pass by. It may be taken as a rule (and rules always have exceptions) that a dozen corporations, each making a separate product, will do better alone than if combined into a single great corporation. The single corporation can never manage all the units as well as each unit could manage itself. But this is not to be regarded as fixing the limits of management, but only as determining the nature thereof.

As a natural development of more intricate manufacturing, it has become apparent that, although there are very few limits to management, there are other considerations which, while not restricting the size of a corporation, do limit its functions, and that therefore it is not always in the interests of the best and most economical manufacturing for any one institution to attempt to do everything with all materials from the source to the finished product.

This is only another way of saying that the theory of what has been called the vertical trust should be carefully examined before it is applied to all forms of manufacturing. It is positively wasteful for some companies to attempt to span the whole distance from source to finished product for all requirements. Every company should know all about everything that goes into its product, but this is quite different from saying that it should control everything. Such control might result in hindering the improvements that independent business men could make in special lines.

Public attention, when it is not on the dangers of machinery, seems to dwell on the dangers of corporate size. Every so often someone gets the notion of a corporation that will control anything and everything and will be a monopoly. The size of a corporation is limited by its market and its function. In a very simple product a corporation can own all the producing and selling machinery from the raw material to the finished product. As the product becomes more complex, such an organization would become less and less economical, for then a certain portion of the activities get away from central management.

The control of the designs and the methods of manufacturing are with us vital. The improving of the design, the material, or the methods of making the smallest part on the car are major matters demanding the best attention of every man in the company. Other matters of routine or recording nature can be delegated. They are only consequences of manufacturing. Once we find the right way of doing anything, then it makes no difference at all in management whether we construct one line of machinery or a thousand lines. And also it does not matter as to the part of the world in which the line is located.

The actual making and assembly of the car itself is standardized throughout the world. The machinery is everywhere the same, and by training men at Detroit we can send them anywhere and they will be at home in the equipment that they find. Any assembly or other plant can be checked at Dearborn.

The managing of a big thing is not more difficult than the managing of a little thing. The big thing may be the easier to manage. It is not size but the possibility of relating all the activities to a single point of control that matters. If the activities cannot be so related, then their management cannot have that exactness which is necessary to the best and most economical work.

It is sometimes necessary for a company to manufacture everything that it uses—that is, to start with the raw material and end with the finished product. This is necessary if, for instance, the supplying manufacturers insist on making to their own design instead of to the designs that are furnished them, or again if the supplying manufacturers try to gain extra profits by higher prices whenever they think the traffic will bear the higher prices. The business of this country is, however, every day becoming more enlightened and is throwing off traditions and is every day more willing to produce exactly according to plans and schedules and to press for reductions in cost while at the same time raising wages. If the product of a manufacturer is at all complex—and an automobile is a very complex production—a specialist in a part will

L

make that part better and cheaper than will a factory which turns out a great variety of articles. The rule that one product is enough for a factory holds for every single part that enters into the construction of an automobile— or anything else. Therefore it is our policy to let out a very considerable portion of our production. Fully 5,200 manufacturing concerns in the United States do work for the Ford Motor Company. We make some of every part that we use in order to keep control of methods and of costs and to experiment in the bettering of each part, but we make the entirety of very few parts. And as a rule we do so only when we cannot do otherwise.

We have to take the lead in a new thing and develop according to our exact needs. When we are finished and in production, the trade catches up, and in a short while is offering to make for us some of the numerous articles we are making for ourselves. But without our equipment and ability to go ahead, without our previous thought devoted to design and method of production, this coöperation of other manufacturers with us would not be helpful. This should not be so; we should be able to ask any manufacturer in any line for any special thing that we want and should be able to get it. But there is a curious inertia in many lines of manufacture which makes a starter necessary.

Always we retain the means of providing for ourselves, so that we can press ahead with changes and not be met by a flat refusal to change. This is in addition to the assurance which we have of not being held up in our production. If anyone can make any part of our product better and cheaper than we can make it, that is a good reason for using the facilities of that one for the supplying of our needs. We do not give up our facilities, but we do not extend them. Extension, however, takes place by the mere fact of our using others' facilities. This is very different from the thought of trying to supply all of our needs under all conditions out of our own resources.

For instance, we need a definite grade of wool for our upholstery and we had trouble in getting it. So in 1926 we sent our own wool buyers into Michigan, Ohio, and Indiana, gained data on all the flocks, and contracted before clipping for all the wool in the districts that met our specifications. We have our own woollen mills which make exactly our grades of cloth very cheaply. But we are not going into the sheep-raising business or into the woollen business. What we should prefer is to get out of them. We go into these things only when we cannot otherwise get what we want and are compelled to demonstrate that it is possible to get what we want. We had to do the same thing with glass making because we could not immediately induce glass makers to change their methods to give us the finest plate glass at the lowest price. They insisted on adhering to their old methods. So to get the methods we built our own glass plants, and we now have four plants making plate glass according to our requirements and our costs. But we would rather have someone else do our glass making. Our coal mines in Kentucky were forced upon us by the fluctuations in the price of coal and by the frequent coal shortages that occurred. (By the way, many of them controlled shortages.) We believed coal could be mined in a fashion conforming to our standards of work and pay. We sell some of the coal and a great deal of the coke, for coal with us is not a fuel but a raw material of chemistry. We sell many of the by-products such as benzol and ammonium sulphate. But we did not acquire mines because we wanted to go into the mining business. We would rather leave that to the mining companies. However, when mining becomes a hindrance to industry, there is no choice for industry but to do something about mining. No one can be permitted to hold up the march of supply.

There is no point in centralizing manufacturing unless it results in economies. If we, for instance, centred our entire production at Detroit we should have to employ about six million people. That would be far too many people to gather in one place only for the making of a single product—the six million people should be spread all over the land in order that every community may be made prosperous by their earnings and expenditures. A product that is used all over the country ought to be made all over the country in order both to save transportation and to distribute buying power more evenly. For many years we have followed the policy of making in our branches whatever parts they were able to make for the area that they served. A good manufacturer who makes himself a specialist will closely control his production and is to be preferred over a branch. Therefore we let out as much work as we possibly can and will probably continue to do so as long as we find coöperation.

At the moment of writing we have, as I have said, 5,200 independent concerns working on our plans and according to our methods. Of these, 3,500 are kept pretty continuously busy on our work. There are two things no one ever does for us, nor will be permitted to do, namely, to make our motor and to set up our cars. These processes are entirely in our own shops, along with something of every other process.

The small independent company has a wide field open to it as supplementing the larger company, and it is not out of the question to conceive a general set-up in which the central company would be more in the nature of a laboratory, assembly plant and general clearing house of ideas and money than a centralized producing unit.

The eventual ideal is a complete decentralization in which most plants will be small and so situated that the workers will be both farmers and industrialists. That would make not only for a more general independence on the part of the individual but also would make for cheaper goods and cheaper food. The present distinction between industry and agriculture is a temporary one brought about by the restricted areas in which power formerly could be had. When power will be available everywhere through electric wires then industry and the workers in it will be set free. The industrial city is only a passing phase of industry. Management will gradually learn to take advantage of its larger opportunities.

CHAPTER XI

CHANGING OVER AN INDUSTRY

THAT modern manufacturing is more flexible than the old manufacturing has been demonstrated by our experience in shifting from Model T to Model A. The shift was not merely one of style. It was fundamental. We undertook to make an entirely new product in an entirely new way. Also we just about doubled the accuracy of the making. This involved the revamping of the largest machine plant in the world. In addition to this we moved all of the machinery out of what had been the largest plant in the world into another plant which then became the largest. Within about six months we were in partial production; within a year we were in full production.

Modern industry is divided into two great classes. The first class makes a single product—or, if it makes more than one product, it makes them in separate factories—and forms its whole organization around that one product. In effect the whole equipment—the company itself—is one big tool for the making of the product in the best and cheapest way. The second class of industry makes only to order and is in the nature of a great general machine shop creating special tools of various sorts—ranging from a lathe to a whole power plant or rolling mill. The second class of industry is in a way subsidiary to the first, for most of its products are designed to meet its needs.

In the first-class industry the whole thought is toward manufacturing a product in the most economical fashion consistent with the highest quality. This style of production has been called "mass production," but actually it is "service production." If ten thousand hand looms should be assembled under one roof, then certainly the production would be massed. But it would not be service production.

Service production can extend only to such articles as can be consumed in large quantities and are of actual service and utility to the people. No one knows just what these articles are, for their number is constantly increasing. One of the best signs of our times is the steady march of former luxury articles into general consumption as necessity articles. Watches, bathtubs, central heating, and automobiles are among the many articles that have made the journey because better methods of manufacturing have brought them within the price range of the mass of the people.

Our company was the first to apply the principles of service production to delicate and complex articles of machinery. At first it was said that the method was peculiar to our company, and then, as the whole automobile industry followed suit, it was said that the methods could be used only in the making of automobiles. But now nearly all commodity articles are made in the same fashion, and it is generally recognized that only in this way can high quality, low prices, and high wages be achieved.

Essentially the method has to do with the making of a single standard article, and then building machinery and arranging processes so that the article may be manufactured with the greatest possible economy. Anyone who concentrates upon the single standard article is bound continually to find new and better ways of making the article —provided that the thing be viewed as a whole and freshly. The basic difference between the older manufacturing and the modern is that the former viewed the machine as an aid to the man, while the latter views the man as an aid to the machine. The earlier industry did not understand the function of the machine, and neither did the political economists. The financiers did not then and, to a large extent, do not now understand that merely owning a large number of machines is something very different from directing an industry.

In service production—which is so erroneously called mass production—the making of the product is dominated by engineering and not by finance. The plan is to subdivide the work into as many divisions as may be necessary for its most economical production, and then to treat each of these subdivisions precisely as though it were a kind of specialty factory, arranging the work sequentially so that raw material enters at one end of the line and emerges as a finished thing at the other end. The parts pass from machine to machine in their making and finally converge in an assembly line, where they are joined together to make a unit. For instance, our motors are formed on an assembly line which is the confluence of a great number of machine lines that have made those parts and also of some minor assemblies. The rear axle, the front axle, the steering gear, and so on are made in exactly the same way. The subsidiary assemblies meet in a final assembly line, where they become an automobile.

Some of the parts join this final assembly line from factories hundreds of miles away, while the final assembly line itself in our main factory at the River Rouge is only a local unit to supply local needs. The various parts made at Detroit may, instead of going into a final assembly line, there go into a freight car or a ship and join an assembly line somewhere else in the United States or at the other end of the world. In our first experimenting with this form of service production we thought that we had to have the machine lines with their assemblies and also the final assembly all under one roof, but as we grew in understanding we learned that the making of each part was a separate business in itself and to be made wherever it could be made the most efficiently, and that the final assembly line could be anywhere. This gave us the first evidence of the flexibility of modern production, as well as indication of the savings that might be made in cutting down unnecessary shipping.

It will be noted, however, that this subdividing and decentralizing of manufacturing made necessary a kind of accuracy utterly unknown to the older industry. The older industry could grind two pieces of metal together until they fitted, but it could not grind a million pieces so that any two would fit as exactly as though they had been ground together. Accuracy and interchangeability are fundamental in the higher development of service production. Interchangeability alone represents a perfectly tremendous saving over the old hand fitting. It is in this unit method of manufacturing, with interchangeability of parts, that the reason for the flexibility of modern industry will be found.

The complete product must begin, for the sake of economy, with a single standard design from which no deviations are permissible. It is enough in the beginning to learn to make one thing in one way. If we had permitted any choice of colour or design in Model T, at the very beginning, we could not have made the low price at which we intended to sell. We broke the manufacturing into units, but the volume of our production was too small to allow any variation of the units. For instance, take the simple matter of colour or body style. A large variety of automobile bodies may be devised, and all of them will fit the same standard chassis. The making of a good automobile body in quantity requires heavy, accurate machinery and skilled work. If one is making a thousand cars a day, it would not be economical to have many styles of body, for each style has to go into an entirely separate division of manufacturing, unless of course all have certain parts alike. In such case these parts would be made in a single division and then divide into assembly lines representing the styles of body. If the production of cars reaches ten thousand a day, then a wider choice of bodies may be made without affecting the economy of manufacturing, for then we have a sufficient production to make use of experience tables as to what body styles and colours customers will ask for, and without going into any freak styles we can arrange in advance our unit production schedules so that the whole production will be a cross-section of the public demand. We can set up what amounts to a factory for each body style. In point of fact, some of our body styles are made by outside manufacturers on our designs. We thus gain a flexibility of style for the purchaser without going into special manufacturing to order—which would of course be impossible in a product to be sold at a low price. Exactly the same rules apply through all of the units which together make up the complete unit; and, though we still keep a wholly standardized product, we can so assemble the various units as to give a very wide choice to the eventual buyer.

Just as these units can be arranged to give a choice to the buyer, so can they be changed in the interests of better designing or better manufacturing—always providing the resulting unit is interchangeable with the one it replaced. It has been thought that service production or mass production is a fixed and inflexible method of procedure. It is so in operation, but it is split up and departmentalized so minutely that very radical changes can be made in any one unit without making necessary the revision of all the manufacturing. As previously noted, we have through the years been making sweeping changes in the design of Model T parts and their methods of manufacture—but without at any time interrupting production. We would simply make more of a part than the schedule called for and then, while these were going into assembly, make all the necessary changes in the department so that by the time the old style part had been used up the new style one would be in production. Every automobile manufacturer does this, but we chose never to call our revised products new models because the new parts were always interchangeable with the old; and, since the process of change was continuous, it would have been unfair to the buyers in, say, January to announce a new model for August. We could have announced a new model each month.

We kept this up for nineteen years and then decided upon a complete revision of our product, its method of manufacturing, and the places where it should be manufactured.

We decided to revamp our entire industry from top to bottom, and to do it all at once instead of spreading it over several years. This revision was not, as has been commonly imagined, wholly concerned with the product but rather with the methods of making and with the general arrangement of our industries.

We had two major choices. The one was to compromise with the new design and with the methods of making in order to interrupt as little as possible the continuity of the factory operations and consequently the employment of our own working forces, as well as the working forces of those from whom we bought parts, materials, and supplies. The other was to make a clean sweep in as short a time as possible, and to keep as many men as we could engaged in the transfer operations, but with the full knowledge that we should have to let some men out. We hoped not to decrease our payroll at any time by more than twenty-five thousand men.

We should have preferred from purely personal motives to make the changes gradually and keep a large force of men employed. But there were other and larger considerations. Most prolonged unemployment, if traced down, does not spring from the adopting of new methods but from the retention of old ones in the thought that continuity of employment must not be severed. And any company which adopts that policy will in the end find itself without business enough to employ anyone. We do not think it wise to preserve obsolete methods rather than have brief periods of unemployment due to making changes, for wise and necessary changes result in long periods of employment. A

short and sudden period of unemployment shows up strik-
ingly, but the gradual decrease of employment due to
hanging on to old methods does not show, and so the
emotionalists do not pay much attention to it.

We were not without experience in this. Back in 1908,
when we put Model T into the new service production,
we had a first-class automobile machine shop that was
as good, for its size, as any in the country. We could have
saved that machinery and gradually worked into the new
methods of making Model T. But we could not have made
it at the price we had decided on, and that price was then,
as now, an integral part of the design. We estimated that
it would take two hundred and fifty thousand dollars to
refit the shops according to our plan, and that was a great
deal of money in those days. But we decided to make the
plunge, and almost completely refitted with special machinery according to our own designs. The result was the
founding of that new practice in production which is
known as mass production and which has had a great deal
to do with the prosperity of the country. We put out that
two hundred and fifty thousand dollars at a time when it
was said that a good low-priced automobile could not be
produced, and that we were throwing away our money in
trying to make one.

In going into Model A the money question did not bother
us. We did not know and did not care how much the changes
would cost. We had plenty of money, and all that money
had been contributed by the public as a result of the quality
of the automobiles that we had turned out. We regarded
that money as in the nature of a trust fund, and the terms

of the trust were that we should always continue to put all
that we knew into low-priced transportation. In 1927 we
did not have the money problem that we had in 1908.

We felt that going into the production of Model A was
an even more important step than going into the production
of Model T, and that if we did the job aright and all at once,
the results in the end would be just as beneficial as with
Model T. That has proved to be the case.

We therefore decided to shut down with the completion
of the fifteen millionth Model T and change over to make
ready for Model A. We, of course, continued to make parts
for Model T, and that was a very large business in itself.
And always we are doing a great deal of building—for instance, in 1927, which was the year of the change, we added
a million and a half square feet of floor space just in the
ordinary course of business. We decided that Highland
Park, which had been our largest plant, was becoming
obsolete, and that we should centre our operations at the
River Rouge plant and move out of Highland Park all
of the machinery which might be suitable for the new
car, leaving only the making of some of the Model T
parts there for the time being. The matter of shifting
about machinery is not at all difficult, for we are doing it
all the time. We simply picked up the machines with
electric cranes and loaded them on cars, and from the cars
they were transferred in the same manner to foundations
already built for them at their various destinations—
whether in this country or abroad. Doing all this was just
a matter of detail.

For the making of Model T we had in service in the Detroit area about forty-five thousand machine tools, of which

thirty-two thousand were production tools. The others were
in our toolmaking departments and did not enter into the
picture, except that we had to add materially to them for
the new work of retooling the plant. That retooling involved
about seventy per cent of the production tools, for, while
Model T had 5275 parts, Model A had 5580 parts, and
practically all of them were different. The new methods and
the new machinery will be taken up in a later chapter in
more detail. Partly they had to do with new ways of making
and partly with new standards of accuracy.

We have already abandoned the whole power plant at
Highland Park. It embodied the best practices of its time,
but we had to have more and cheaper power for our electric
furnaces and for our new electric welding processes, as well
as for running all our machinery. Therefore, we expanded
the power plant at the River Rouge plant and installed four
turbogenerators which gave us a total of two hundred and
fifty thousand horse power. This is more than double the
amount of horse power that we had previously used—which
gives an indication of modern industry's demand for power.
We have made provision for four more generators.

The new methods of making required the installation of hot-metal spinning machines, which make possible
the use of fabricated steel where castings were formerly
used. These machines are somewhat on the principle of a
potter's wheel. Hot metal discs are placed between vertical
rotating dies, and in a few seconds turn out an almost finished part of much greater strength than would be possible
in a casting. We went very much farther than before with
power presses. The largest press used on Model T weighed
something over two hundred thousand pounds. Some of the

new presses we installed weighed more than half a million pounds. In Model T we had been working toward forging and stamping with an increasing amount of welding. But ninety per cent of Model A is composed of steel, and with an absolute minimum of cast parts. Most of the parts are forged, pressed, or spun. These give lightness and strength, but they involved some wholly new departures in welding.

We could in most instances have fitted our new design to the existing machinery, but that would not have been as economical in the end as disregarding our machinery and taking a fresh start. The new machinery is in the line of future progress; and, if our experience with Model T is repeated, steady and substantial improvements can be made in the future without sweeping plant changes. It pays in the end to do a thing aright.

In addition, new assembly lines had to be created for each of the many assemblies that go on to the final assembly. But in all of this we have had a long experience. Viewed as a whole, the job was large, but if a single machine be designed, made, tested, and found to be right, then any number can follow. And then one gets into the old swing of trying always to improve.

At this point some of the lessons that we learned in the general process of fundamental change may be stated. They seem to be of universal application. They are as follows:

(1) The steady pressure to improve methods and product will eventually lead to a new product in order to embody all that has been learned.

(2) This change is not to be made lightly and never to be made merely to give what is called a sales argument—the

sales argument is, as always, in the product and not in its trimmings.

(3) In addition to setting aside funds for ordinary repair and replacement, a balance is needed in hand for the very large changes which time will bring about.

(4) That it has not been necessary to change any of our fundamental principles.

CHAPTER XII

FLEXIBLE MASS PRODUCTION

ONE of the largest difficulties in manufacturing—or in anything else—is to avoid self-satisfaction. If one does a job well, it is only human to sit back and look it over with satisfaction. In this sense success is the enemy. It is hard to regard the job that has been done as only a temporary stage from which to give one's attention at once to doing it better. Here is an interesting letter on this very point from one of our foreign-born workmen:

In 1921 I was working with an installation crew of one of the largest German electrical concerns on a light and power line in an old castle belonging to the Grand Duke of Baden. Four of us were working with one of the best leaders the company had.

Walls, often one foot thick, had to be drilled. This is nothing unusual, as practically all German houses have heavy brick and stone walls. Electric wiring in Germany is installed along the ceiling. Standing on a ladder one has to break the holes through with chisel and hammer. Often it takes hours to make a single hole.

The main cable had to be laid through a cellar wall four feet thick. Lying flat on the ground and working with a plain chisel and hammer it took us three and one-half days to break this hole through. Disgusted with the job I said to the leader: "Why doesn't somebody design some tools to facilitate this work?" A rather typical reply followed: "We have always made those holes in this manner; we always got them through. The old method is all right; why try to change it? Such tools as you suggest would soon put all of us out of work."

We worked hard but accomplished little in a day. Our pay was small, barely sufficient to cover our living expenses. We all belonged to the union, and I remember many a talk along the line: Our wages are too low, and prices are too high. (The leader received about four dollars a week, the men between two and three dollars.)

One evening I mentioned that I would soon leave for America. "I guess you'll soon be making lots of money and ride in an automobile like a millionaire, while we are wondering how to get enough to eat," said one of my fellows. "They have everything over there, because they won the war."

Some months later I stood at a factory window in Highland Park. A conveyor, parts, motors, wheels, fellows busy—a few hundred yards farther—an automobile. I looked and watched for hours. An air hammer, a tractor, and an air compressor, how easily we could have broken in a few minutes that hole through that wall with such tools. I thought again of that foreman's remark: "The old method is all right; why try to change it?"

I applied for work in that plant; I got it.

I saw new machinery, new processes, new methods constantly being introduced. I heard of price reductions and wage increases, but I have never heard anybody say: "We always made the holes in this manner; we always got them through—the old method is all right, why try to change it?" I never heard this sentiment in America.

Even I, though I am not a millionaire, can to-day afford my own car, because there were some people who said: "Let us make those holes a little faster," and thus brought down the cost of cars, of houses, radios, washing machines, etc., so far that even the worker can afford them.

So I have learned from my work, that the American people are prosperous and receive high wages, not because they won the war, but because they are always looking for better and faster methods to do their work instead of pinning their hopes for a better living on political strifes and machinations.

That man had caught the spirit of forward-looking American industry more accurately than most of our own people. Indeed, many of the political and social movements of to-day in this country when coldly analyzed could be expressed in the words of the foreman or leader whom this correspondent describes: "The old method is all right; why try to change it?"

We all know that a man or a company which adopts

every new thing that comes along is in the position of
always getting ready to go somewhere but never being
quite ready to go. There is a difference between adopting
something simply because it is new and adopting it because it is better. The leading manufacturers in America
—and this is most particularly true of the automobile industry—are ready to adopt a new thing almost regardless
of its cost as soon as it has been adequately demonstrated
that it is better than anything which has gone before. In
the Ford industries we regard an improvement as only a
step forward and never as the realization of perfection. We
try out everything that seems to offer the chance for
further improvement. Take any five-year period and at the
end of the period no part, no machine, and no method in
our industries will be the same as it was at the beginning
and some will have been changed many times. Yet for
every change that we make we may reject, after careful
examination, a hundred or maybe a thousand suggestions.
There is a difference between an open mind and one that
is just gullible.

Volume or mass production will defeat itself if it be
allowed to become fixed, rigid production. Our company
for nineteen years, as far as the world was concerned,
made only one product—the Model T car. The company
made this one type of car through all of those years
for exactly the reason why it is not making it to-day. I
experimented with a great many different types of cars
and actually sold twenty thousand cars in eight models
before settling on Model T. Some of those cars were fours
and some were sixes. The reason for Model T was the
same as the reason for Model A and needs some ex-

plaining because there seems to be a great deal of confusion concerning the flexibility of mass production.

We completely changed our product even to the smallest detail of method and material. We did not simply get out a new model of a motor car, for we have been doing that right along. On October 1, 1908, we brought out the first Model T car, and on May 26, 1927, we closed that experience with the fifteen millionth. Not a single part in the final car was of exactly the same design as the same part in the first car, or made of the same material or by the same methods, but over reasonable periods all parts were interchangeable. This complete change had taken nineteen years. Then in five months we made changes far more sweeping than had taken place over the nineteen years and went into an entirely different kind and grade of production that involved new methods and materials and forced us to get rid of or materially alter seventy per cent of our machinery. In the course of this work we picked up our entire tractor factory and took it to Cork, Ireland. Also we picked up what had until then been the largest automobile factory in the world, put part of it into another factory— and that without interfering with the production in either the first factory or the second. We sent what machinery we could not use in the second factory out to other factories which we created or which were in existence in this and foreign countries. And in the meantime we had to change over and give new training to about two hundred thousand workmen. The net result was that in a year and a half we produced the first million cars of the new series. It took Model T ten years to reach its first million.

Model T was not the best automobile that, at the time,

I knew how to design. It had to be a compromise. The roads then were bad, and a car had to be made which would run through anything. The people of the country did not know anything about automobiles or any other kind of delicate machinery. They distrusted the ability of anyone but an engineer to run any kind of an engine. Therefore the car had to be very simple in its operation and easily repaired. It had to be sold at a low price, but also to be durable. The state of engineering was such that there were almost no facilities in the way of machinery for turning out in quantity so precise a mechanism as even a crude automobile must be. Quantity production, up until that time, had always been crude production. We are still very far from mechanical perfection in anything, but back in 1908 machine production was very crude indeed.

It was very generally said that we could not make Model T for the price at which we brought it out and that shortly we should fail. That price was twelve hundred dollars. During the years we sold that same model greatly improved for as low as two hundred and ninety-five dollars. We made that model according to this creed, from which we have never found it necessary to deviate:

(1)   An absence of fear of the future and of veneration for the past. One who fears the future, who fears failure, limits his activities. Failure is only the opportunity more intelligently to begin again. There is no disgrace in honest failure; there is disgrace in fearing to fail. What is past is useful only as it suggests ways and means for progress.

(2)   A disregard of competition. Whoever does a thing best ought to be the one to do it. It is criminal to try to get business away from another man—criminal because one is

then trying to lower for personal gain the condition of one's fellow man—to rule by force instead of by intelligence.

(3) The putting of service before profit. Without a profit business cannot extend. There is nothing inherently wrong about making a profit. Well-conducted business enterprise cannot fail to return a profit, but profit must and inevitably will come as a reward for good service. It cannot be the basis—it must be the result of service.

(4) Manufacturing is not buying low and selling high. It is the process of buying materials fairly and, with the smallest possible addition of cost, transforming these materials into a consumable product and giving it to the consumer. Gambling, speculating, and sharp dealing tend only to clog this progression.

It is a far cry back to those early days of Model T. It is almost impossible now to visualize conditions. The driver's seat in those days was on the right. For sound reasons which we had worked out we inaugurated the left-hand drive. It was as revolutionary in the people's imagination as driving backward would be. A long time was required to accustom the people to the idea and induce them to give it a trial. They would not give it up now. This generation, born to the left-hand drive, may regard it as a trifling matter, but we who engineered the change know how difficult it was. In 1907, the year before Model T came out, road repair was largely a local function. Now the country's annual road bill is in excess of a billion dollars. Down in the South they used wide carts, and they wanted an automobile with a six-foot two-inch tread so that it would run in the ruts. Our car therefore was of necessity a pioneer car: it appeared in the era before good roads. The automobile became the most powerful of all instances in building and improving roads. With the great change which came in road conditions throughout the country many of the pioneer requisites in automobiles became unnecessary. Greater refinement became possible. It was like the progress from the covered wagon to the carriage—when pioneering conditions passed, refinement of manufacturing processes became naturally the next step.

There is a difference between a need and a wish. The public may need a thing and not know it because it has not yet seen the thing that it needs. The public needed the automobile long before it wished for it. The estimate of the need was not wholly wrong. The stimulation of a proper desire was only ordinarily difficult. But it is not within reason that a single basic model should forever continue to meet the need of a progressing world. Model T met that need for nineteen years—although it would not have met it had not the changes in it been continuous. In the last year of full production—which was 1926—we made and sold 1,800,000 cars.

In the years since the first Model T went out, the country has built roads and the public has learned to handle machinery. The use of automobiles has taught the half-grown boy as much about machinery as most skilled mechanics knew twenty years ago. In the making of automobiles we have learned a great deal. We have learned how to use power and to shift the requirement for mechanical skill from operating the machinery of production to the making of that machinery. We now have materials of a strength and lightness that were scarcely dreamed of twenty years ago. Above all we have learned to design productive machinery which will work to a high degree of accuracy. The last Model T sold for less than a third as many dollars as the first Model T, but it was three times as good a car. In fact it was a car which in 1908 we could not have built at any price. Yet that final car had in it only a part of what we had learned. Therefore we had to make a large decision.

With roads came the opportunity for greater speed and a lower centre of gravity. The public has learned enough about automobiles to handle speed. These changes in need, it will be noted, did not originate with the public, but have been brought about by the improvements in the automobile. The education of the public and our own education had been going on together.[1]

---

[1]This is the record of Model T during nineteen years—its contribution to the welfare of the country.

The company paid wages, plus salaries, to a total of $1,970,414,172.29. This is exclusive of the entire year of 1918, when the company engaged largely in war work. This represents an average pay roll of $100,000,000 per annum for nineteen years.

But this is only a fraction of the income which the Model T created for workers. Maintenance and service employees of dealers, salesmen, employees of service stations, outside garages, and repair shops who have serviced or worked on this car all must be considered. These swell the amount paid in wages and salaries to a total of $5,467,614,172.29.

The total purchases made by the company in connection with the manufacture of the Model T as well as by the Canadian company and by the foreign and American branches, came to $4,868,427,012.32. Statisticians have figured that between 33⅓ and 40 per cent of this sum represents wages or salaries paid to employees. Using the lower figure as a basis, the sum of $1,622,809,004.10 is obtained, which brings the previous total to $7,090,423,176.39, wages and income directly attributable to the Model T. Such a sum of money is difficult to visualize. It is greater than the estimated wealth of thirty-five of the forty-eight states in the Union. This would mean a pay roll of $373,180,167.18 each year for nineteen years. Even this does not include the train workers, the rubber and oil workers, and countless others.

Those figures show what a single idea will do to the wealth and income of the world—and how footless it is to look back to schemes for redistributing wealth when we can look forward to creating wealth. There are undiscovered industries lurking everywhere. The world is only starting—not stopping.

The original car expressed part of what we knew at the time, and we have been working up from that. It was a question whether to express all we knew in a drastic and fundamental overhauling of what we had or to start from the ground up on something entirely new. We decided on the latter course.

This meant more than changing a model. It meant changing a base. We could, without a great deal of difficulty, have designed a new model which would not have required more than a change in the details of the methods of production. Such a model, however, would not fully have utilized what we had learned. We decided not only to make a new car but to take advantage of the opportunity to make it differently. These new methods of making were not primarily required by the design of the car, but we concluded to do everything at once in order that as many as possible of the men, who necessarily were released from production, might be employed in construction.

The change of base is very important in large-scale production, for once we had settled on a base we could then work forward again, just as we had with Model T. It is our policy to do all of our testing in advance of production. If we can get one car exactly right, then we can make one million or ten million more precisely like it—and they will not need testing. We use all the known laboratory tests, but no amount of laboratory testing will substitute for the actual tests in use on all sorts of roads and in every kind of weather. Thus we used up hundreds of cars. It was expensive—but not so expensive as going ahead with less than the utmost of knowledge we could obtain.

The details of the changes in design are not important, for they are technical, and also they are well known and available to anyone interested. The point is that all the major changes were the result of manufacturing knowledge that we had gained. In our new designs we deliberately went ahead of anything that we or anyone else had ever tried in volume manufacturing. We took as a goal the making in large quantities of a grade of work that had never before been done except by the most skilled workmen on the highest priced products.

We did not simply stop business and change over to make a new model. We only stopped assembling and selling Model T cars. We kept on making the parts, and anyone could have bought the parts and made a new car if he cared to. There were ten million of them on the road then; there are over five million registered now. In fact, we continued, in spite of going out of the production of new cars, to conduct a very large business.

The moving from Highland Park to the River Rouge, for instance, had been going on for some years. With everything else being changed we just hastened the process. For concentrating all the heavier operations in the one plant saved us the moving of some twenty-five hundred cars of freight a year between the two plants. That saving had long been planned, but we did not finish the moving until long after production was well under way. The moving was one of the biggest moving jobs the industrial world has ever seen, yet it was accomplished so easily that even in the city where it was being done few persons noticed it.

[NOTE: All the departments at Highland Park—equipment, machines, and men—had to be relocated, and the already existing equipment and machines in the new locations had to be considered, rearranged, sent elsewhere, or otherwise disposed of. Machinery was sent to assembly plants outside the Detroit area and even across the sea. Plant layouts were changed; new construction was done, and at the same time new electrical hook-ups were made, new foundation pits dug, new conveyors installed, new balconies erected, and equipment already in place rearranged. This amounted in some instances to a complete realignment of existing production means, because of the addition of the machinery from the older plant. Furthermore, this was executed without interrupting the flow of production of Model A cars and Model AA trucks. In fact, while the removal was in progress, production steadily mounted day by day.

The transfer of operations from Highland Park to the Rouge plant is nothing new. In the fall of 1927, the final assembly line was moved over. In its new location it occupies only one half the space formerly used, although it produces just as many assembled cars. All of the heavier assemblies and parts are now brought by conveyor from their place of manufacture to the proper place in the assembly line, and it is no longer necessary to ship motors, the chassis, and the body parts to Highland Park by rail.

More than a dozen new steel balconies, some of them of considerable length, had to be built in the Rouge plant and more are under way. In the south end of the foundry, four were set up to accommodate incoming machines, and many have been installed in the rolling mill and others in the motor building.

The new conveyors built in the Rouge plant form a subject in themselves. The plant now has more than twenty-seven miles of conveyors; and many of the new ones are especially interesting, such as that spanning the transept of the rolling mill, taking ring gears directly to the finishing machines, and also that which carries the rear axle assembly from one building directly to the freight cars on the tracks outside.

Some of the departments now entirely moved were the largest of their kind in the world. The tool rooms were enormous, while other important departments were the roller bearings, ball bearings, axle shaft, gear, steering wheel, die casting, cold heading, drive shaft, radius rod, universal joint, front spindle, and brake drum. In 1924 Highland Park was described as "the largest automobile factory in the world in production." The radiator department, it was said, "was capable of producing more radiators than all other radiator manufacturers combined." The spring, axle, or steering wheel departments, "if freed from Ford production demands, could supply the balance of the entire automotive industry." All of these were moved.

At the same time, the Highland Park tool departments merged with those at the Rouge plant, and also a rearrangement was effected so that efficiency was increased and yet the number of departments and men employed was reduced. A total of eighteen departments was reduced to fourteen, and a more scientific use of floor space enabled the departments to cut down the area required from 667,984 square feet to 595,252.

The machinery and the departments were all moved on the same plan of procedure. In advance came the men responsible for the relocation to check the floor space against the number of machines allotted, and to arrange the placing of the men and work to the best advantage. The men and their work were transferred ahead of the equipment itself, the work being so divided that it was going on in one plant while another part was closed off for removal. The workmen on arriving at the Rouge were temporarily located in whatever available space was nearest their job, pending the completion and installation of their own layout. Since production could not be tied up at any time, all this required careful planning.

The heavier machines were brought on railroad flat cars and the lighter ones on trucks. In transferring the tool room equipment, as many as twenty-five to thirty-five machines a day were moved. This involved the use of large crews of men for different purposes. Electricians were busy making connections and hook-ups. Much new construction work had to be done. Some of the biggest machines, such as the huge rotor mill forty-eight feet long and weighing about one hundred tons, had to be taken apart and shipped in sections. Pits fifteen feet deep had to be dug for some of the machines. Most of the larger sections had to be skidded. In the south wall of the Foundry Building, doors had to be cut both higher and wider. Five new cranes, two ten-ton and three five-ton, had to be installed in the foundry.

, New steel balconies had to be erected to take care of some of the departments. Along the south and southeast sides of the foundry may now be found one of the largest tool departments in the country. Here, close to the power house, it can handle the maintenance of turbine parts. And here also will be overhauled and rebuilt all of the production machines from the Rouge lines. The old-time practice of performing that work near production has given way to the concentrated shop where experienced men and special machines are available. The tool room will keep up its own tools as well as those of the plant.

The die-casting department, where small production parts are cast directly from dies, moved from Highland Park to a corner of the Foundry Building in the Rouge plant. In its work it uses combined furnaces and machines; it works with aluminum and zinc; it nickel-plates; it makes more than forty different Lincoln parts; it makes its tools and dies and die-cast dies, as well as its own die-casting machines and fixtures; it turns out miscellaneous parts ranging from metal handles for screw drivers to spools for the wire job. Each day it devotes two hundred hours to aircraft parts work, and it is one of the few places in or near Detroit where aluminum and zinc are being nickel plated. These are just a few of its functions.

All its machinery, together with materials and equipment needed to keep the department in full production, was moved during two week-ends. Seven hundred men and about three hundred machines and an entire tool-room department were included in the transfer. This department was one of the most complex to move, for it had a most varied equipment. For example, sixty-two low-pressure die-casting machines had to be connected with air, gas, water, and, finally, with a new suction system. Each of these with its fixtures weighed about fifteen hundred pounds. With each went a metal bench, hood, and stack or draft pipe leading up toward the ceiling like the ordinary stovepipe, and joining with other pipes into a main line which had also to be erected.

Two preheating furnaces had to be built and set up for melting the gates and scrap created within the department itself and used again in making castings. Each furnace has a capacity of nineteen hundred pounds of metal which is dipped out six to eight times a day. These furnaces are of an original design and have an egg-shaped combustion chamber in which sits a cast-iron pot for holding the molten metal. A partition divides the interior into hot and cold sides, with a hole at the bottom through which the metal may pass. After the aluminum has been taken out, the dross is removed from the dross chamber and is sold.

After casting, the parts are sawed, trimmed, polished, and otherwise finished. Among the machines used in these operations are band saws, punch presses, screw machines, automatic machines, drill presses, as well as polishing jacks. All these had to be set up and connected properly. To insure the efficient handling of work, they had to be placed in such fashion that the work would move progressively; and a conveyor had to be installed to carry the castings in baskets from operation to operation and to return the gate and scrap back to the preheating furnaces. That meant a conveyor completely around the department, together with a running monorail. Four more die-casting machines, using high instead of low pressure, had to be set up and connected.

Consider for a moment the suction system that had to be installed. A stack 120 feet high had to be projected through the foundry roof; to this central draft all of the die-casting machines and preheating furnaces had to be hooked up. This in itself was a sizable job, yet it was only one of the incidents connected with the moving.

Then there were the twenty-five tanks used in nickel plating. Sumps had to be constructed for supporting them; generators had to be erected and running to provide current for the anodes; piping and plumbing had to be installed; hot water had to be available for steam.

Fully seventy-five per cent of the parts cast in this department are of aluminum alloy and eighty-five per cent of this is reclaimed from the piston borings scrap. Parts include the light switch for the Model A, the gasoline gauge dial and frame, the water pump bushing—speedometer drive cap, deck steps, fan pulleys, carburetor adjusting rods, and so on. Zinc parts include the window handle, the door pull handle, and the windshield knob. Above five tons of zinc are used here every twenty-four hours, mixed with about 250 pounds of copper scrap. Zinc burns easily, hence in the nickel-plating process the parts are held in the solution by racks which are agitated gently, rather than dipped in and out by a conveyor.

Altogether, more than one hundred and twenty thousand parts are produced every day in this department. When it is considered that these are inspected, and in many cases boxed, wrapped in tissue paper, and shipped, one realizes the scope of work covered in its removal during two week-ends to new quarters.

While all of this was going on in Detroit, the assembly plants throughout the United States and the world had to be changed, and within less than eight months ninety-four per cent of these plants had been changed and were in production—that is, thirty plants. The first Model A came out

N

of assembly on October 20, 1927. It was offered to the public on December second, and by November 1, 1928, the production had reached more than six thousand cars a day and 186,313 men were being employed, of whom 125,000 were in the Highland Park and River Rouge plants.

As a result of shutting down and making a clean sweep, the business has so increased as to need the direct help of about one hundred thousand more men than before. The scale of wages is gradually increasing; no man gets less than he did before and many get more. At least one hundred thousand men, in addition to those above, are, as a result of the additional requirements, employed throughout the country. Against these gains the losses of shutting down are scarcely to be calculated.]

CHAPTER XIII

The Changing Scene

THE moving of what had been the largest automobile plant in the world and the placing of all its departments in another plant which was already supposed to be full showed us many economies that we might effect. It is the little things that are hard to see—the awkward little methods of doing things that have grown up and which no one notices. And since manufacturing is solely a matter of detail, these little things develop, when added together, into very big things.

For instance, when we designed our power plant at the River Rouge we went ahead of existing practice in many respects and particularly in making feasible the burning of powdered coal. We planned a certain number of units and took for granted that each unit required a certain amount of space. In this we followed custom. That was in 1919. But constantly we have been needing more power and finally we had to double the capacity. And since building an additional power house would have been expensive, we decided to set ourselves to doubling the capacity of the power house we had. Into a space designed for a turbine capacity of 65,000 kilowatts we put in a turbine that we designed and built ourselves to develop 145,000 kilowatts. The turbo-generators develop 30,000 kilowatts each. To meet this additional load, it was essential that the boiler capacities be increased; but additional boilers would require a heavy investment in buildings and equipment, as there was no space left in the power house for additional boilers. Accordingly, we remodelled the original units and more than doubled the capacity of each of four units. In other words, the completion of the remodelling was equivalent to the construction of two large power houses in a single building while it was already occupied by units which were among the largest in use anywhere. The whole matter of saving space without crowding has been pressed upon us by the telescoping of the Highland Park plant into the River Rouge plant. We have always placed machines close together and tried to cut down to a minimum the movement of any part during the course of its manufacture, but until this removal we did not really know what it was to save space. We only thought that we knew. We had the same space-saving problem at a number of our branches, and it was the request of a branch for additional space which would have cost nearly half a million dollars to provide that brought our attention to a matter which we had considered as standard.

Formerly, open and closed bodies each had ovens, conveyors, flow stations, sash inclosures, and suction systems of their own. Experiments indicated that a single system of ovens and conveyors would do for both types of bodies and that only minor changes would be necessary to accommodate them. We had no difficulty in merging the two systems. The same ovens could be used for either open or closed types. And the saving was remarkable.

In less floor space than was formerly needed to turn out one hundred jobs under the old method in eight hours, a branch now can produce 180 cars. Some idea of the amount of saving made possible by this change can be gained from the statement that the average per branch was somewhere near seventy-five thousand dollars during the first year. The entire job is concentrated in one system, making possible closer supervision and giving the employees greater versatility. The new system produces more cars than the two systems did before. In the particular branch that originally caused this study, the adoption of the new plan enabled it to dispense with eighteen thousand square feet of additional floor space which otherwise would have been required.

Here is a very different matter. Dies have always occupied a prominent place in production process where forgings or sheet-metal parts are stamped or pressed out, and their manufacture and maintenance have comprised one of the big jobs of production. For example, one die required about seven hours to make and had to be replaced after it had shaped about forty thousand pieces. We devised a new method which can turn out a die impression in two minutes and each die will shape from eighty thousand to one hundred thousand pieces. The former method of die manufacture used an engraving or profiling machine in which a master die guided tools that engraved a duplicate of the die on a steel block. Then the block went to the bench for finishing, for the engraving machine left marks on the impression. Because of the human element, it was impossible to secure two dies that were exactly alike.

Under the new method a hardened master die is driven into a heated block of steel, much as a seal is driven into heated wax. An exact impression is made of the master die. When cool it is polished and edged, after which it is ready for use. The reason for the longer life of the typed die over that of the engraved is in the grain of the steel. The engraving tool cuts into the grain of the cold steel, whereas the new method, by heating the steel first, renders it plastic and the grain is molded to conform to the impression.

Placing a washer on a screw has always been a hand operation. We devised a little machine for this and have made some very great savings. When it is remembered how many thousand washers must be handled in this particular operation every day, it can be seen that the accomplishment of such a job by machinery was worthwhile. The screws slide down a tilted incline from a square container. At the lower end they are seated by a set of jaws that set them into place, one at a time, into one of the openings in the circumference of a revolving drum. Just before the screw drops into the opening a washer is fitted to the hole, sliding off the bottom of a perpendicular rod that, with its row of washers, somewhat resembles an ancient Chinese money counter.

When the screw drops into the hole it is fitted to the washer. The screw then remains in position on the drum until it has revolved around to a point where it is released in such a way that it turns a flip-flop somersault and lands, head up, on an incline opening onto a slotted tray. The latter consists of rows of grooves made to fit the screws, each tray capable of holding twenty-five hundred at a time.

The operator removes the rod when all the washers have

slid off and replaces it with another that has been filled meanwhile through a shaker operated by air. He also operates a lever that controls the slotted tray and moves it along from groove to groove as each in turn is filled. A simple device prevents jamming. If an·odd-size screw gets into the chute it is thrown out by the automatic "kickback" just outside the hopper at the top of the incline. The machine is spring driven so that nothing can jam it. Currents of air are used to deliver the washers to the drum and to loosen the screws from it after it has revolved around to the point of release. This machine saves much monotonous labour.

Electricity, by providing a new motive power, has profoundly changed manufacturing. As a source of heat for furnaces and the like it has made further changes. But even greater things are at hand. These are revolutionary. Wages could not be what they are to-day if we were still compelled to rely on the old shaft and pulley. That not only limited the speed of a machine and wasted a great amount of power but also it restricted the placing of the machines. Everything had to be in the line of the shaft instead of in the line of the work. We were considered too hasty when we first built an electric motor into every machine in the shop and also when we took advantage of the perfectly controlled heat made possible with the electric furnace, but these practices have become the industrial commonplaces of to-day. Consumption, production, and wages to-day hang on the industrial use of electricity.

The new and revolutionary use of electricity will in its extensions cause goods to be made much stronger and more cheaply than ever, which will have direct effect on consumption, production, and wages. This is the use of electricity for joining parts together without bolts or rivets—that is, by welding.

This goes to the very root of all metal manufacturing and is the first absolutely new basic method of manufacturing that has come forward in many years. We have taken old methods, improved on them and changed them about until the final method did not look at all like the original method. But with electric welding we strike out into a new field. And here again we have inescapable proof that modern machinery is labour serving and not labour saving. For these machines do what man absolutely could not under any circumstances do.

The only way that anyone in the past knew to make an intricate metal article in one piece was to cast it. Casting is very wasteful. It requires the heating of the metal and then a deal of highly skilled work with patterns, cores, and all the paraphernalia of the art. The casting of each piece had to be a separate operation and, although years ago we put casting on a production basis and used the method of subdividing the work and taking it to the man by conveyors instead of having the man go to it, yet at the best the operations were crude. A casting must be machined—sometimes to taking away thirty per cent of the metal; that is a waste. And also there is no way of knowing just how strong the casting is, for there may be blow holes or other defects that cannot be discovered.

A part may be forged or stamped out of hot steel of some standard mill size, and the part will be stronger than a similar part which is cast. Everyone has known that for years, and for years we have been forging and stamping as many parts as we could. We know that if we could build up a complicated part by joining a number of small forgings we should have something stronger than could be had by casting. But we had no method of joining other than by bolts or rivets and that method of joining is not only expensive but requires such an excess of metal to hold the bolts or rivets as to make the resulting part less practical than a casting.

The art of welding is very old. It consists of heating two pieces of metal and hammering them together. The old blacksmith was an expert welder. The electric weld follows the same principles, but the heating is by an electric arc formed between the two parts to be joined, and the pressure is applied mechanically. Electric welding has been known for a long time, but no apparatus has existed for taking the human skill out of the operation—that is, for putting pieces through by machinery in great volume at a low price. We set ourselves the task of devising machines and methods that would make possible the wide use of welding as the best and also the cheapest method of manufacturing. We wanted to forge, spin, or stamp parts and then build them into complete units by welding. That we have done. The subject was not new to us; we used some welding on Model T, but during the last three years under the pressure of necessity we have progressed farther in welding than during all the previous years of the company's existence.

Welding makes possible the uniting of forgings and stampings into integral parts of strength, lightness, and symmetry at a speed unequalled by any other known process. There are many kinds of electrical welding, but we are concerned with resistance welding, which is divided into flash welding, spot welding, and seam welding.

In flash welding no metal is added. Only the original metal is used, and in heating is fully protected from the oxygen in the air and other impurities. There is no difference between the *theory* of the old-fashioned blacksmith weld and the electrical resistance flash weld. The blacksmith put his steel in a forge and the heat was applied externally. When at the proper heat it was removed, the surfaces to be joined were cleaned of oxide, placed together, and hammered vigorously. The actual welding was accomplished by heat plus pressure.

In resistance flash welding the heat comes from an arc drawn between the surfaces to be welded. As they will not heat sufficiently to weld except through the heat of the arc between the surfaces, it is necessary to have the pieces of a nearly uniform cross-section. Copper jaws conduct the current to the piece to be welded. The amount of flashing is determined by experience. Zones in the pieces to be joined are protected from the oxygen and other impurities in the air by the arc, and the section is speedily heated to the proper welding temperature. Then the two pieces are forced together very quickly with enormous power. This squeezing also forces out any overheated metal that may be left, allowing the clean metal to make contact. The same principle is carried out in the other two types—seam welding and spot welding.

Progress in electrical resistance welding is progress into the unknown. This is particularly true of butt welding, a type of resistance welding that finds wide and important application in our industries. The worker in this field must begin with the idea and end by building the machinery to carry it out. There is, in nine cases out of ten, neither knowledge nor machinery existent to suit his purpose.

A seam weld is actually a succession of overlapping spot welds, usually made on a machine in which the object to be welded is drawn between copper disks placed edge to edge, through which the current flows.

In every case where welding has been adopted it has made possible the decreasing weight without decreasing strength, and to lessen cost of manufacture without lessening quality. Further, it has immensely facilitated the accurate and precise adaptation of the proper material for the proper part.

Take a few experiments in electrical welding that have been brought to a production basis and are in daily use. Take one half of the rear axle housing assembly. It consists of four individual parts welded into one integral unit whose entire weight is only eighteen and one-half pounds. The small spring perch is a steel forging, machined accurately, and the ball for the shock absorber hardened. The wheel housing is also steel forging, rough machined, and the wheel bearing hardened. They are placed in a welder and flash welded together at the rate of one hundred and fifty per hour. The burr, or "flash," is removed in a special machine, and the part is ready for the next operation of welding to the tube, which is done at the rate of one hundred per hour.

- The tube is a piece of sheet steel weighing seven pounds, four ounces, that is blanked in wedge-shaped form from a large steel sheet formed in three operations on a punch press, and then arc welded longitudinally at the rate of fifty tubes per hour. It is then restruck to insure uniformity of size and shape and is ready to be flash welded to the bell end forging. The rate is sixty per hour.

This bell forging is a development by our men and is made by hot rolling or spinning a blank of hot steel between two formed rolls at enormous pressure and high speed, the procedure forming a graceful curved bell uniform in thickness at no sacrifice of strength. The four pieces have now become one through welding. Each is machined in line with the other and will always maintain that alignment and rigidity.

The rear axle housing is one of the most important of our welding developments. In the Model T the rear axle housing was made up of malleable castings. The same assembly is now electrically fabricated of forged, pressed, and spun-steel parts, each adapted by special treatment to the function it is to perform. The differential housing or "banjo" is composed of a U-shaped section of steel—a standard rolling-mill form—pressed by dies into a circle not quite complete. The circle is closed by the differential housing sleeve, which is made in a forging machine and welded to the unconnected ends of the U section by the flash-resistance method in a mechanical welder of our design and construction.

Take the differential housing assembly. Here a casting has been eliminated in favour of the all-steel housing made possible by welding. A part made by a punch press is welded to a forging and we have here developed an automatic welding machine. A description of this new type of welder will show how welding engineering along this line is advancing.

This is a summary of our old method: The channel ring is placed in its cradle and aligned, the removable clamps are dropped into place, and a valve is turned which releases the air into two cylinders that in turn actuate the clamps and pull the ring against the electrodes on each side. The operating handle is pushed back from the loading position to open or starting position. The neck is slipped over the expanding collet, which is also the electrode, against a locator and aligned, the forked clamp is slipped into place and the air is turned on, expanding the collet. The actual welding procedure now starts. The operator grips the handle and throws the trigger switch, turning on the current. He burns off the abutting ends of the neck and ring to get an even contact. Then for three or four seconds the ends are held tightly together and preheated. The arc is then drawn between the parts by backing off the handle enough, so that the current leaps the gap drawing an arc. The operating handle is now brought up evenly and steadily to maintain this arc to a predetermined point, the correct heat being the determining factor, at which time it is pulled home as quickly and vigorously as two husky fellows can manage. The air is then released, the three clamps removed, the operating handle is pushed back to open position, and the housing lifted out, completely welded. Three operators are necessary for each machine, production twenty-five to thirty per hour.

That procedure is just as complicated as it sounds, and the operators require careful training. In our new machine the principle is the same, but the operator's duties consist in placing the stock in the machine, slipping on a clamp, and turning the air valve, which clamps all parts at once.

The machine then goes through the welding cycle automatically to completion. The air valve is opened, and the machine returns to its starting position, where the housing is removed and the operation repeated. This machine requires only one operator and does from fifty to sixty an hour. And the welding is more uniform.

The new machine is completely foolproof. All working parts, except the clamps, jaws, and other equipment for handling the work and applying the welding current, are contained cleanly in a single large housing, where they are, however, readily accessible through doors. All parts outside this housing are inclosed in a large hood, having a door which is closed while the actual welding operation is in progress. While the welding operation is in progress, fan-shaped plates, operated by cams, cover in turn all operating buttons except the one needed for the next move. It is impossible for the operator to go wrong.

Here is another automatic welder. In it the operator is relieved of placing the lugs in position by hand. They are loaded automatically from a magazine and are set in position for the weld through the use of a magnet on the upper jaw and a locating fixture on the lower.

The operator's hand is protected from the possibility of getting caught in the machine. Besides this factor of safety, the machine makes it possible for him to turn out work much more rapidly. Under the old system the average number of brake shoes one man could handle per hour in this operation was two hundred. That was when he loaded the lugs by hand. This has now been more than doubled; four hundred and fifty an hour is the regular number welded. That means nine hundred welding operations, owing to the fact that each end of the brake shoe has to be welded. Each end requires two lugs, one on each side, a total of four lugs per shoe or eighteen hundred every hour. Since each lug has four projection points, these eighteen hundred lugs require seventy-two hundred during the hour.

Lugs are welded on the brake shoes to reinforce the ends, where holes are bored. Under the old system the operator inserted the lugs in position, placed one end of the brake shoe between them, and completed the weld. Then he removed the shoe, inserted two new lugs, set the other end of the shoe between them, and completed the weld.

The new machine feeds lugs into proper position along miniature tracks so arranged that new lugs do not take position until the previous operation has been completed. They are held in position by magnets, and the position of the brake shoe between them is controlled by the machine. The shoe can be fitted readily by the operator almost without watching.

In developing the magazine many problems had to be overcome. One was to keep it free from the attraction of the magnets. Otherwise the whole mechanism would be interfered with and the lugs would jam in the grooves. To prevent this the magazines are made of brass, which is nonmagnetic. Just before the current is turned on for the weld, the magazine is swung out away from the magnetic field.

Forty-four power presses are required to form each gasoline tank assembly and prepare it for the seam-welding operation, as well as much other equipment. Ten presses blank and form the bottom; six prepare the top; sixteen are required for the speedometer cable housing and other fixtures; two form the splash plate; three rivet fixtures to the tank; one clips top and bottom together in position for welding; six punch holes and restrike the form.

When the two sections of the tank have been clipped together in position for welding, and the work on holes and restriking is completed, they are further secured by spot welds placed at intervals. They are then washed in a strong alkaline solution and placed on a conveyor. On this they are carried past workmen who add the retaining quality of solder to that of the rivets which secure the fixtures to the tank. From this operation they pass to the welding machines.

No single unit has undergone such a revolution since its beginning as that of the ring gear. The ring gear stock used by the company to-day is rectangular. It is cut to lengths equal to the circumference of the gear. The lengths are heated and placed in machines, which form them into a circular ring, leaving a small gap between the ends. The rings are completed by being butt welded while red hot. To relieve the strain under which the steel has been placed, the rings now receive an annealing or normalizing heat treatment and are allowed to cool slowly.

The scale that has accumulated on the rings during the cooling process is removed by tumbling. Boring, counterboring, back and angle facing follow, all these operations being performed by automatic turning and boring machines. Ten cap-screw holes are drilled simultaneously in each gear on a multiple spindle drill press, after which the rings are ready to have the teeth cut in them.

The teeth are first roughed out on special machines. The gear-roughing machines formerly in use were capable of operating on but two units at a time. The present ones, which are equipped with auxiliary equipment of design, rough out twenty-four gears at once, removing approximately a pound of metal from each gear and taking slightly over two minutes per unit for the job.

Next the gears go to machines called generators, where they are given a finish cut. The type of generator formerly in use required a separate operator and, at best, produced not more than fifteen gears in eight hours. The department used thirteen of these, giving a total production of less than two hundred gears per eight-hour day. To-day the department has ninety-six high-speed generators and ninety-five of improved standard type. Each high-speed generator produces forty-three gears per eight-hour day, and eight can be tended by one man giving a production per operator of 344 gears per eight-hour day.

In the modern gear generator the gear is mounted on an arbour and the teeth accurately lined up between cutting tools, so that an equal amount of stock will be removed from each side of each tooth. The tools travel across the face of the gear tooth at the rate of four hundred strokes a minute, removing a very small amount of stock at each stroke, to insure the best finish. As the machine finishes the last tooth—the fortieth—it automatically shuts off.

Ring gear steel is of the highest quality and has a large carbon content, so only a cyanide treatment is necessary to give it a hard wearing surface. Coming from the cyanide furnace the gears are quenched in oil in a gear-hardening press of our design, to prevent distortion. Two men, one on the furnace, the other on the presses, can harden and straighten 1,960 in eight hours. When cold enough to be handled without gloves, the gears are removed from the press and subjected to another drawing operation, which relieves the strain involved in the cyaniding.

Now the bores are ground out on internal grinding machines, on which the gears are mounted with master gears to insure accuracy of bore. The limit of deviation from accuracy is one thousandth of an inch. At the conclusion of the grinding operation, the gears are passed on for a test in which they are rolled with drive pinions for quietness. They are now ready for assembly or service.

Formerly three inspectors were required to check four thousand gears in an eight-hour day. Now one inspector, with the aid of an automatic testing machine, checks six thousand in eight hours. A device on hand gear testers makes it possible for one man to roll thirteen hundred gears per eight-hour day. A few years ago six hundred was a satisfactory day's work.

The ability to combine parts by welding means the introduction of a whole new technique into metal manufacturing. We have just started.

CHAPTER XIV
A Millionth of an Inch

THE making of things to a high measure of accuracy is not just a test of workmanship. It is a fundamental to service production. In such production there can be no fitting of parts in assemblies or in repairs. Every crankshaft must be exactly like every other crankshaft and so on through every part of the automobile or anything else that one may be making by this method.

Of course, no two parts are ever absolutely alike except by accident, for it does not pay to try for accuracy beyond a certain point. But any kind of a machine which has moving parts must be accurately made or there will be an amount of vibration through play that will shorten the life of the machine and also decrease its running efficiency. A designer always plans a machine made to absolute measurements, and then he sets the limits by which each part can be allowed to vary from the measurements. In volume production the measuring has to be done quickly, and for that reason each part is judged by two gauges of whatever designs prove most suitable for the part. These two gauges represent the allowable limits of size. If the part passes through both it is too small, and if it passes through neither it is too large; to be within the limits it should pass through one and not the other.

Some parts do not require accuracy in any high degree, while others must have limits of one ten-thousandth of an inch. If a gauge is going to check to one one-thousandth of an inch—which is not extreme accuracy—then that gauge must itself be accurate to at least one ten-thousandth of an inch. And it must be kept accurate. Thus there must be a master gauge to test it—and finally a gauge to test the master gauge. All of which presumes that somewhere on the premises one has some absolutely accurate measurement with which to test the master gauge.

In point of fact, it was not always possible to know what an inch was until we had C. E. Johansson join us. And to-day the functioning of our industries depends upon what goes on in a small room in the Dearborn laboratories. And so also does the functioning of many other industries, for in this room are tested the precision blocks not only for our own use but also those that we sell to other industries, for it would not be in line with our policy to keep the means of accurate measurement exclusively with us. These measuring devices are available to anyone who wants them, and they are the standards of all accurate work in this country and in most parts of the world. The obtaining of a standard of accurate measurement is not so simple as it might seem to those who measure with a foot rule and think they are measuring. The finest steel rule made is so inaccurate that, if we had to use it, we should wreck our production. That gives some idea of our necessity for accuracy.[1]

Until recent years there has been no way of attaining

---

[1] The material that follows in this chapter is based on Mr. Johansson's description of this most interesting science and has been read and revised by him.

a real accuracy in machine production. For we have had no standard inch for shop work. It is service production that has forced the making of standards of accuracy. The English foot of twelve inches was legalized about the year 950, but fought for more than three hundred years before it supplanted the Belgic foot of the Tungari, which was 13.22 inches, and was brought to England at the time of the Belgian influx before the Tenth Century. The origin of the Belgic foot is lost in the obscurity of ancient Asia and Greece.

The metric system is the result of a demand by French scientists that the unit of measure be based upon some measurable and immutable distance in the universe. The French National Assembly chose a distance equal to one ten-millionth of a quadrant of the earth through Paris. This distance was duly computed, and the resultant *mètre-à-traite,* or measure of distance, known as the metre, was made the compulsory national standard in 1801. In 1875, the International Bureau of Weights and Measures was constituted in Paris to furnish prototypes of the metre to subscribing countries. The official French metre is represented by the distance lying between two microscopic lines on an iridio-platinum bar (now reposing in the archives of the Bureau), at zero centigrade.

The alloy and the cross-section chosen for this rod are least susceptible to change. Temperature is a vital factor in computing the metre, since, as the temperature of the rod goes above or below zero centigrade, the distance between the scribings becomes less or greater than a metre. The consideration of temperature was one of the great problems previous to the advent of the Ford-Johansson gauge.

The metre is measured at zero centigrade; the English inch at sixty-two degrees Fahrenheit, and the U. S. inch, by Act of Congress, July 28, 1886, at sixty-eight degrees Fahrenheit. Considering these temperatures it is evident that, to bring the three standards into accord, the units must be held at three different temperatures. If a standard (French) 100 mm. steel gauge, at zero centigrade, having a coefficient of expansion of .000,011,5 per one degree centigrade, is measured at the English standard temperature, *it is .019 mm. longer than 1 decimetre.* Measured at the U. S. standard temperature, *it is .023 mm. longer than 1 decimetre.* Conversely, a U. S. standard decimetre gauge and an English standard gauge become correspondingly less than a decimetre when measured at the French official (metric standard) temperature.

Since these standards of measure have been adopted, another method of checking the accuracy of measures has been discovered. The instrument used is called an interferometer. Its operation is based upon the constant length of the rays of light in the spectrum. Should the official metre gauge be destroyed, it might be reproduced within one ten-millionth of its theoretical length with the aid of the interferometer. This instrument has shown that the metre is equal to 1,533,164.13 wave lengths of the red ray of the spectrum of cadmium in the air at fifteen degrees centigrade, and 760 mm. barometric pressure. But of what avail is such a method of measuring in a machine shop?

Less than forty years ago most of the difficulties experienced in commercial measuring in mediæval times still existed. Each country, each large industry, and even each toolmaker had individual measures. While these measures all conformed to either the metric or the English standards, no two agreed unless made from the same material, in the same shop, and at the same time. Each shop had its own set of master gauges from which measurements were sometimes taken directly, but more often these gauges were used to make other individual gauges for specific work. Since gauge making was slow, expensive work, it followed that a shop doing any volume of business had an accumulation of gauges that represented an investment out of all proportion to the amount of use which they received. The matter of the investment, however, was only incidental to the gauge difficulty.

When a gauge is made of steel it must be hardened to withstand even moderate use without appreciable wear. When a piece of steel is hardened tremendous internal strains are set up within the surfaces of the gauge which cool and set first as the gauge is quenched after heat treating. These strains are gradually relieved by slow expansion of the metal—a process that may continue for a year or more after the gauge is completed. Also if a gauge is not used at the same temperature as that at which it was finished its size will vary with the difference of temperature.

Thus, what with a variation of standards, a variation of materials, and a variation of temperatures, the paths of the machine and tool manufacturers were anything but rosy. Arguments between a mechanic on the warm side of a shop with one on the cold side often became legal battles between seller and buyer which involved broken contracts, months or even years of litigation, and often not inconsiderable damage awards by courts. The court decisions could never establish precedents, for they were rendered arbitrarily for lack of any universally recognized standards of measure.

C. E. Johansson began his career as a mechanic in Eskils-tuna, Sweden, in 1885, and as tool-room foreman of the government's arms factory he first faced the problems arising from an inaccurate system of measure. Although well equipped with the usual quantity of gauges, scales, and measuring devices, the arsenal did not adopt the tolerance system of measures until 1889, when they undertook the manufacturing of arms, in the present-day sense, in place of the highly individual method of arms manufacture which obtained from 1867 back to the days of the stone axe and arrow makers. During the period 1867–1889 the arms were manufactured by machines, and although the quality was good the quantity production was limited because the limit system was not used.

One of the first points which impressed him in those days was the preference of toolmakers for solid blocks of steel finished to a specific size corresponding to some specific dimension to be imparted to the manufactured part. Scales varied in their calibration and micrometers varied in the leads of their threads, but once a machinist measured a dimension to a steel block, and it was accepted, he worked speedily and confidently to the block until it was worn out. Consequently, Mr. Johansson specialized on these solid gauges. Soon there were hundreds of them in the arsenal and hundreds more being made all the time to take their places. At each change in specifications, from two to a hundred of these became obsolete—most of them long before they were worn out. Though inches, half inches, quarter inches, and the like did not change, parts could not be designed to suit the existing gauges—gauges must be made to suit the designs.

Mr. Johansson, from his experience, knew that two gauge blocks, if finished with the most painstaking care, would adhere slightly when wrung together. A close study of the finished surfaces of such blocks held a promise that several gauges might be made so accurately and so perfectly finished that they might be used separately or in combination to produce from one to a number of measure values limited only by the number of gauge blocks used. He began work along this line at once, but almost immediately another difficulty was encountered. No method for determining the size or the parallelism of the surfaces of these gauge blocks was accessible. Hours of work were necessary to measure any gauge, and even then the margin of error was great. Eventually it was solved in a manner that permitted the instant gauging not only of the flatness and the parallelism of the opposite surfaces of a gauge but the determining exactly how far these surfaces were apart. However, as this end was approached, a new difficulty became increasingly great; namely, the stabilization of the steel itself from which the gauge was made, a difficulty which seemed insurmountable.

Unless a gauge block is heat treated and hardened, its usefulness is soon greatly impaired by wear. In the case of a gauge the accuracy of which is required only within one one-thousandth of an inch—and it is now a quick and simple process to divide this accuracy by ten thousand, measuring to one ten-millionth part of an inch—this accuracy would be completely lost with very little use unless the gauge were rendered glass hard by an adequate heat treatment. It became evident, when working in such small dimensions, that a block which was heat treated and finished to within one ten-thousandth part of an inch of the measure value desired, would begin to expand, very slowly, after it was finished, until at the end of a year it might measure several ten-thousandth inches more than when finished. The larger the block and the greater volume of steel it contained, the greater the growth after finishing.

By the year 1899 gauge blocks could be made by Mr. Johansson so flat that they would adhere when wrung together. Their surfaces could be placed at a predetermined distance from each other within a margin of a few hundred thousandths of an inch. The surfaces of the blocks could be rendered so nearly parallel that, when placed in combination, the cumulative error in several blocks was no greater than the error in a single block of the same length as the combination. Selection of the steel best suited to the manufacture of gauge blocks and the discovery of the heat treatment which would render this steel sufficiently stable required experiments over a period of nine years. Then a universal gauging system passed from an ideal to an accomplishment.

The first set produced contained 102 blocks. Years of observation had shown that the temperature of the average machine shop varied between fifteen and twenty-five degrees centigrade; therefore twenty degrees centigrade

(sixty-eight degrees Fahrenheit) was selected as the standard temperature at which these and subsequent blocks
should be finished and used, except blocks made for use at
specified temperatures other than sixty-eight degrees
Fahrenheit.

Sets of these gauges were introduced into the United
States in 1907, and were received with some hesitancy. Purchasing agents at first considered them too fine for their
requirements. Even if they allowed themselves to be persuaded by shop superintendents to purchase sets, they frequently placed them in the office vault and permitted their
use only when a difference of opinion on measures arose.
While American manufactureres were accustoming themselves to the possession and use of gauges, the same gradual
acceptance of this new standard was going on in all foreign
countries. As the gauges became known their possibilities
became increasingly evident. The limit system of manufacture, that is, the process of holding the dimensions of
each part of each assembly between two limiting dimensions
as determined by these new gauges, became universal. Even
the limits became somewhat standardized. Thus, one standard permits a round rod to fit a round hole in four degrees.
These are: running fit, push fit, driving fit, and forced fit.
In the first class, the rod slides in the hole easily; in the second, it may be pushed into the hole but fits snugly; in the
third, a hammer is needed to drive the rod into the hole; in
the fourth, a mechanical or hydraulic press is needed to
force the rod in. In the first, or running fit class, standard
practice requires the rod—supposing it to be more than 1"
and less than 2" in diameter—to be less than the diameter of

the hole by not less than .0015″, and less than the diameter of the hole by not more than .0025″, or a limit of variation of .001″, the difference between the two tolerances. In the case of a driving fit, the limit changes from less to greater; the diameter must not be less than .00075″ greater than the diameter of the hole, nor more than .002″ greater, or a limit of plus .00125″; the limit on the case of a forced fit is plus .002″.

If rods similar to the one described were to be used in quantities, a gauge for measuring their diameters would be made. For the rods the gauge would consist of four pieces of steel, set in a horseshoe-shaped holder, two far enough apart to allow the rods to pass between them in their diameters were not greater than the maximum tolerance specified, and the other two close enough together to keep the rods from passing between them unless the diameters of the rods were below the low limit prescribed. Such a gauge is called a "go-and-no-go," or snap gauge, and the points may be spaced to the specified distances apart by setting them to gauge blocks, or combinations of them, of the measure value desired.

The accuracy of practically every manufacturing operation carried on to-day may be traced directly to the use of these gauges. The Ford Motor Company has one hundred and forty complete sets in daily use, besides a quantity of single blocks for purposes where complete sets are unnecessary. This number does not include many pocket sets individually owned and used daily to test the accuracy of micrometers.

The alliance of the C. E. Johansson Company with the

Ford Motor Company furnishes an interesting chapter in the development of the gauges. Considering the importance to the Ford Motor Company of high accuracy at a low cost, the gravitation to it of the C. E. Johansson Company, with exactly that combination, was inevitable. Also, by means of the resources and the manufacturing talent made available the price of the gauges has been materially decreased since the Johansson Company was taken over.

Thousands of gauges and fixtures must be manufactured in our tool rooms, and by using these blocks it is possible to make them to the necessary limits. Without the Johansson blocks and tools our tool rooms would be blind. By using them the gauge inspectors also can tell at any moment the condition of the gauges and fixtures in service.

How important this is may be realized from the fact that, when one of the gauges is worn to the point it no longer checks the limits properly, one hour's run may mean several thousand pieces of scrap, tying up of the assembly line, or the holding up of some branch in a remote part of the world.

If extreme accuracy is to be obtained economically—as mass production demands—the master standard gauges must be just as near to size as it is possible to make them. Any error in the master is multiplied several times before the working gauges reach production. When production machines or the assembly lines are held up for minutes, or the fraction of a minute, the cost is very high. Every error in a gauge must be paid for in the slowing down of machinery and the loss of parts.

Take, for example, the snap gauge used in the manufacture of the push rod in the car. These cost approximately four dollars each to repair; twenty are used on each eight-hour shift, and their life is approximately four hours. On all gauges twenty per cent of the tolerance is the wear limit. That means a wear limit of one ten-thousandth of an inch or one hundred-millionths. Hence, it costs one dollar for each twenty-five millionths of an inch wear.

At least three sets of Johansson gauge blocks are needed to pass these gauges every time they are sent to the tool room for repair. One is used by the man who repairs; another by the tool-room inspector; and a third is used in checking them every four hours. If an error of many millionths exists between the three sets, more gauges would be returned to the tool room than actually wear out. Production would be retarded and costs would run high. Therefore, we have determined that it pays to hold the master gauges to the extreme accuracy of not exceeding plus or minus two millionths of an inch. Thus the inspection gauges for the tool room and for inspection have an accuracy of plus or minus four millionths, and working gauges can be supplied the production line at an exceedingly close limit, well within an accuracy of fifty millionths of an inch. All of the close-limit gauges used are checked once every day, many of them three times every eight hours. Under the guidance of Mr. Johansson himself, the workmen are able to control degrees of accuracy at a saving. He believes that it is no harder with proper means to hold to a close limit than to the old accepted accuracy.

We have searched practically the entire world for special gauging equipment. Much of this is reconditioned by the

Johansson division after it is received. And it is a large undertaking to get dies, jigs, and fixtures together to build accuracy. A large proportion of the machinery we use must be rebuilt to meet the accuracy standards.

One of the chief requirements in the gauging system is a definite manufacturing—wear tolerance, established and maintained. The first thought, of course, must be accuracy; the second, speed. The third is the original cost, plus the amount of repairs and reconditioning necessary. There must be some swift, accurate way to determine when it is time to retire a gauge from use. For this, our men use the Johansson block.

The manufacturing of these blocks is carried on in the Dearborn laboratory, and they must be finished at a temperature of sixty-eight degrees Fahrenheit. This requires a special room. The constant-temperature room in which the finest gauges are finished and tested is seventeen by eleven and one-half feet. Its walls are of plaster to a height of three feet; above that they are of glass. The glass walls are double, with a space of twelve inches between, which serves as an air duct. The glass in the outer wall is of triple thickness, that of the inner of but one. Throughout, the glass is set in heavy felt and hermetically sealed in its frames. The doors, of which there are two, are fitted with weather strips. The walls and ceiling are insulated with two layers of cork, laid directly on masonry surfaces, and the floor is insulated by the same material, laid in asphalt cement. All walls have a four-inch base of cement.

A constant temperature in the room is maintained oy circulating air at the proper temperature in the air duct formed by the double walls of glass. A number of electric elements supply warm air to the duct whenever it is needed. A refrigerating machine supplies cold air. Thermostats at three points control the flow of warm and cold air. The presence of workers in the room reduces the amount of oxygen and adds to the amount of moisture in the air. To make up for the first an ozonizer, having a capacity of six grams of ozone per hour, is used. With this are installed two dehydrators, capable of supplying this room with thirty litres of dry air per hour, by means of which the moisture is counteracted. Mercury tube lights are used for illumination. To prevent their heat from interfering with the temperature of the room, they are separated from it by a case of glass, and the resistance coils with which they are equipped are placed outside the room.

The making of these gauge blocks is an intricate and highly skilled process. Some of the gauges used for shop work are very ingenious, and they must be tested by special apparatus. Take the wrist pin hole in the piston of a Model A motor. It is checked by a special Johansson internal gauge, which in turn is set by a ring gauge. The wrist pin hole and the pin must fit within limits of .0003 of an inch. To test the ring gauge we have a machine that will check the inside walls of a hole. The machine is known as an "inside optometer." It looks like an elaborate microscope. The ring gauge is placed in the centre of the machine on a tiny platform, which can be swung in any direction. It is brought to position beneath two jaws, or measuring parallels, that extend downward toward the floating table. These parallels are set with Johansson blocks, and the distance between is thus known accurately. On the tips of the jaws are jewels, placed there to provide a hard, unyielding contact against the inside walls of the ring gauge. After the parallels have been set against the inside walls of the gauge the operator, by looking into an illuminated tube on the right of the machine, is able to detect whether there is any variance. If the walls are within one half of one ten-thousandth of an inch, the operator can see the difference in greatly magnified degree as through a microscope. It is enlarged so much that the operator can halve the size just mentioned—which is one hundred times finer than the size of a human hair.

This instrument may be used to detect not only a tapering in the walls of the hole but also the exact inside and outside diameters. It can also tell whether a tool or part is out of round, and by how much.

Here is another example. In the use of screw threads many dimensions must be checked to insure proper fits when the threaded parts are assembled. For example, a bolt and nut must fit together. Both the external thread on the bolt and the internal thread in the nut must be measured. That can be done with master gauges made and threaded like the parts to be fitted. With these the parts can be tested during manufacture.

But how to measure the accuracy of the master thread gauges? The answer is found in an intricate-looking machine in the gauge-inspection room. It is known as a "universal measuring microscope." With the microscope in this machine, the screw threads can be magnified to such

P

proportions that they can be easily measured. It is the second machine of its kind to be brought to America; the first is in our Dearborn laboratory.

Checking is accomplished by use of the knife-edge method. The knife-edge is a narrow blade of steel having an angle on one end. On the knife-edge a fine line has been engraved at a given distance from, and parallel with, the edge formed by the angle at the end. In the microscope are lines that have been spaced apart the same distance as that between the engraved line on the knife-edge and the edge of the knife. Two blades of steel are used. The knife-edge of one blade is placed in contact with the flank of the screw.

The other is placed on the opposite side of the screw thread so that it comes in contact with the opposite flank of the screw.

By means of the microscope one of the lines in the eye-piece is superimposed upon the engraved line on one of the knife-edges. A reading is then taken on a magnified vernier scale. The carriage of the machine is then moved until the other line in the microscope eyepiece is superimposed upon the engraved line of the other knife-edge. A reading is again taken on the magnified vernier scale, and the difference between the two readings is the correct pitch diameter.

There are three different phases of a screw, all of which will affect its accuracy, and which all must be measured. These are the pitch diameter, which technically is the diameter of an imaginary cylinder, the surface of which would pass through the threads at such points as to make equal the widths of the threads and the width of the spaces cut by the surface of the cylinder; the lead, which is the distance a screw thread advances axially in one turn; and the angle, which is the angle included between the sides of the thread measured in an axial plane.

All of these phases can be checked on the universal measuring microscope. In fact, since the machine was installed, the accuracy of thread gauges in the plants has improved almost one hundred per cent. The machine will determine whether a surface is absolutely straight and square. It will measure either round or tapering surfaces equally well. It is especially useful in checking templates and in laying out holes. It has been said to measure as fine as one ten-thousandth of an inch.

With a dividing head, this machine can be used to determine angles or indices. The head is placed in position in a specially constructed groove. Through its magnifying lens the operator can look down on a circle, the degrees of which have been so much enlarged that each is divided into three parts and each third into twenty. The operator can thus read the minutes as well as the degrees of the angle and can check within limits of one minute.

These, of course, are not manufacturing gauges. They have to be so nearly absolute in their accuracy only because the gauges in use must be what they purport to be, else the parts turned out in production will not fit. An error at the source is multiplied many times when it reaches the part.

One ten-thousandth of an inch is a workable accuracy, but to insure that degree of accuracy one must be able to control to perhaps a millionth of an inch. That we can do.

CHAPTER XV

THE STORY OF 199 SHIPS

TRUE economy has nothing to do with curtailing use or skimping or otherwise limiting one's life. That is destructive economy. I am interested only in constructive economy—which means getting the greatest possible service out of a thing and then, when that service is ended, looking about to see if the thing cannot be used again in some other service without any great additional labour.

This thought goes behind the thing itself to the labour that it represents. If we do not use to its utmost everything that is made, we fail to gain the full value of the human labour which is present in it. That eventually reacts upon the income of labour, for that income cannot in the end be greater than the values it produces. The hoarding of goods is an indirect method of reducing wages. We find very low wage scales in all the countries where more attention is given to seeing how long a thing may be made to last than to seeing how much use can be had out of it. We in the United States are held by certain foreigners to be very wasteful, but only because they have been trained in destructive economy and cannot comprehend constructive economy—that is, the economy of the fullest use.

Almost everything has a primary use and a secondary

use—and possibly subsequent uses before reaching the junk pile. The junk pile need not be the end; it may be rather a clearing house for materials to go again into manufacturing. Our nation has not as yet seriously taken up the question of finding secondary uses, possibly because many of the materials that have been used have not been good enough to make a secondary use profitable, and then again there has been no organization of sufficient capacity to take up reclamation as a national affair. When an automobile has ceased to have any value as a means of transportation, it is still a valuable collection of metals. If it could be approached not simply with a view to salvage but with a view to finding new uses for the materials that, in even the oldest car, are just as good as new, then we should have a new source of wealth.

In our company we tried out the reclamation of automobiles on a small scale just to find out what could be done, and we learned that the plan was perfectly feasible. We confined our experiments to the Detroit area and did not go into the thing on a volume basis—and that is the only basis that would have had any consequences. We learned enough to know that some day it would be profitable in a narrow sense, as well as very useful in a broader sense, to go into the business of reclamation in a large way.

As a part of a general investigation into the secondary use of materials, as well as into their re-use, we bought 199 ships from the United States Shipping Board, not simply with the thought of salvage, but to see what could be done further to use these ships, not as ships but as structures made up from many valuable manufactured articles and materials. There is nothing new about breaking up a ship. It is an established business in England. But the thought has always been to take out only such parts as still had a value—or, to be more accurate, a sale at second hand—and then abandon the hulk, or, if necessary, tow it out into deep water and sink it. Even this has never been undertaken on a large scale or as part of a manufacturing process. We proposed not to wreck these ships but to take them apart, recondition, and find uses for all the engines, valves, boilers, winches, pumps, motors, tanks, pulleys, injectors, ejectors, cables, chains, and other manufactured articles that could be recovered intact, and to take the steel, brass, cork, wood, tin, asbestos, rubber, felt, canvas, hemp, paper, and the long list of materials that they would produce and, with or without changing their form, put them again into manufacturing.

We proposed to disassemble on a very large scale, and neither we nor anyone else had any experience in this sort of disassembling. These ships represented a part of those built by the Emergency Fleet Corporation to meet the exigencies of the war. The government shipbuilding programme, it may be recalled, was in answer to the German submarine campaign. Our authorities, with a long war in prospect, set out to build more ships than the Germans could destroy so that under no circumstances would our forces overseas or the forces of the Allied powers be defeated for a lack of supplies from the United States. The war ended with the building programme in full swing. It was impossible to stop the programme all at once without serious economic disturbance to the country, and so a certain number of ships had to be carried on to completion. Immediately after the Armistice the world seemed to be short of ships, and the United States Shipping Board went into the shipping business. In the spring of 1920 the overseas freight market collapsed, the Shipping Board began to lay up its vessels, and by 1925 it had a large number of ships out of service and tied up in various rivers and harbours. Of these the Board offered for sale 200 ships. We were requested to bid. We did so and our bid was accepted --the number offered being changed to 199.

These ships were of first-class steel construction. Fifty were of the "submarine type" (the name being taken from the company that built them) and were each 324 feet long with a beam of 46 feet and a dead weight of 5,060 tons. The others were known as "lake type" ships, having been built at shipyards on the Great Lakes. They ranged from 251 to 253½ feet in length, had a beam of 43½ feet and a dead weight of from 3,280 to 4,155 tons. Some of the ships had served in the war, but sixty per cent of them had not been finished when the war ended, and few of them had seen as much as two years' duty. To all intents and purposes they were new ships, but they had been laid up so long that none was in condition to put to sea under its own power. They were scattered all along the Atlantic seaboard. The big ships—the submarine type— were handily located; some were in the James River above Norfolk, others at Hog Island in the Delaware River, and still others in the Hudson River, mostly at Jonespoint, thirty-six miles up from New York City, and several were at Staten Island. Of the lakers, fifty-eight were in southern waters below Mobile, Alabama, with the largest number in the Gulf of Mexico. The others were in the James River, at Hog Island, at Jonespoint, and at Staten Island.

Our job was to get all these ships to Dearborn and there disassemble them in the quickest and cheapest fashion possible. The ships of the submarine type were too large to pass through the Welland Canal, so bringing them all the way as ships was out of the question. It was also out of the question to consider having the ships use their own power. So the job had to be a towing one and it is no small task to tow an ocean liner up the Atlantic Coast into the stormy regions about the mouth of the Gulf of St. Lawrence and thence up the Gulf and the River and through the canals to the Great Lakes. From the Gulf of Mexico this meant a journey of more than 4,000 miles and for the boats at Jonespoint, which was the nearest station, the voyage was 2,329. We considered a great many plans, among them cutting up the ships on the Atlantic Coast and shipping them by rail to the River Rouge, but this plan would have been very expensive. The plan we finally adopted was to cut apart the submarine type ships at plants at Norfolk, Virginia, at Kearney, New Jersey, and at Chester, Pennsylvania, load them on the lake type ships and then tow the ships thus loaded by way of the St. Lawrence to our River Rouge plant.

This involved setting up a production schedule, or rather a disassembling schedule, so that the submarine boats would cut up on the coast in regular order so that there would always be cargoes for the lakers and also so that the lakers could arrive at the River Rouge in regular order so as not to hold up our work there.

We bought seven seagoing steel tugs from the government at a cost of $42,500 each and spent an average of slightly over $12,000 each reconditioning them. We also reconditioned three of the lake ships at New Orleans to move the ships north from the Gulf of Mexico ports. In the meantime we began to make our plans at River Rouge, but were hampered by not having an actual ship to work with. This was in the fall of 1925. Winter was coming on, and it was a question whether we could get a ship through ahead of the ice. If we did not we should be greatly delayed when the ships began to arrive in the spring, for we should not have had an opportunity to test out our plans in actual practice. We decided that it was worth trying to get a ship through, and in the middle of November started the *Lake Fondulac* from Kearney in tow of the tug *Ballcamp.*

The ships survived colossal difficulties, however, and on the night of December thirteenth dropped anchor off Port Dalhousie at the entrance to the Welland Canal. Navigation was officially closed, but special arrangements had been made with the Canadian government to keep the canal open. Two tugs were waiting to help. The start was made early next morning. The boats pushed through relentlessly and on the evening of December seventeenth they tied up in the River Rouge shop at Fordson. The trip had taken just thirty-two days, ten hours, and fifty-two minutes.

Preparations for the major dismantling operation at the Fordson plant were carried on simultaneously with the experimental work on the *Lake Fondulac*. Lessons learned in taking the ship apart were promptly applied in the designing of the tools, in the establishing of methods, and in the training of men. Different portions of the ship presented different problems—the superstructure required one type of work, the plumbing another, the bulkheads another, the machinery another.

Ways for doing a thing better were continuously tried; if the new way proved more efficient than the old, the old was immediately abandoned. Methods were constantly being changed and improved. Work was started on the *Lake Fondulac* the day after the vessel arrived at the plant. It ended June 15, 1926, when the last ship-bottom section was hauled to the storage yard. Dismantling the *Lake Fondulac* took 180 days. Dismantling the second ship twenty-nine days. By the end of the summer three ships were being taken apart every five working days.

Many experiments were tried on the *Lake Fondulac*. The combined force of cranes and powerful hydraulic rams was first used to rip the deck plates from the beams. The rams exerted pressure from beneath while the crane falls, hooked to a corner of the deck plates, tugged from above. The decks were peeled off easily enough by this method, but the plates were left jagged and distorted, and were difficult to handle later. A specially designed roller cutter or shear was used in slitting the side plates of the *Lake Fondulac*. Suspended from a crane, it was lowered over the edge of the side plates to get its "bite" and pulled upward. After each cut the shear was lowered again until a stop rested against the lower edge of the cut, when it was in position for the next bite. The shear was housed in a compact frame, which guarded its vulnerable parts against breakage, and its smooth contour prevented it from catching on projections while being handled.

Hook knives attached to the crane falls were also used for slitting the hull side plates vertically. Both the hook knives and roller cutter worked well, but the torch was finally adopted for most of the cutting work.

With the *Lake Fondulac* in the process of dismantling, the plans for building and equipping the special dismantling dock were rapidly carried out. A boat slip already projected from River Rouge turning basin half a mile into the Fordson plant yards. On one side of this was the ore dock, backed by the storage bins, the blast furnaces, the coke ovens, and the cement plant.

Along the other side the new dock, approximately twenty-two hundred feet long, was constructed. Space was allotted for ten ships in line. Pipe lines for gas, oxygen, compressed steam, compressed air, and water were buried in trenches along the dock.

Three sets of railroad tracks and a set of widely spaced rails including a third rail for gantry cranes were laid down. Feeder tracks were built to the open-hearth furnaces and to the different storage sectors. A large locomotive wrecking crane of two hundred tons' capacity was mounted on two six-wheel trucks, and was capable of lifting an entire engine weighing seventy-five tons, or a boiler weighing fifty tons from its foundation in the ship's hold and placing it on a specially built flat car. The crane was operated by steam. Its weight ready to operate was 366 pounds. This necessitated driving eighty-eight pilings into the ground and tying them together with concrete for the foundation inway of the dock at the point where the crane operated. Each piling was estimated to hold a load of twenty-five tons. There was a maximum reaction at the end of the centre outrigger, thirteen feet from the centre of the crane, of 350,000 pounds. As the crane travelled on standard gauge track it could be moved readily to any part of the plant to unload the boilers and engines from the flat cars and place them in position for storage.

In addition we mounted many other heavy cranes to handle smaller loads.

Instead of hauling up ships on a marine railway as we had at first planned, we had a floating dry dock made to handle the final operations in the disassembling line. As we increased the speed of the operation we decreased the number of men. We had an average of about fifteen hundred men on the job in 1926 and only about a thousand in 1927.

The big movement started when the ice had cleared in 1926 and was fully under way by the middle of April. On each ship we reconditioned one boiler to operate the auxiliary machinery and did all other necessary reconditioning for the voyage and to accommodate a crew consisting of a captain, a chief engineer, a steward, three firemen, and three seamen. We set a trip time of thirty-five to thirty-eight days, equipped the tug boats with wireless so that they could follow the practice of our ships of keeping in daily touch with the home office, and we moved the entirety of these ships without loss of a single life or the loss of a single ship. One ship went ashore, but the crew was taken off and the ship was afterward recovered.

To insure a constant supply, ships were brought from the East in such numbers that a reserve fleet was established in the Detroit River a short distance from the mouth of the River Rouge.

From the reserve fleet a ship to be dismantled was towed about four miles to the River Rouge turning basin, and tied up at the north wall of the slip. Here all consumable stores, foodstuffs, dishes, hardware, furniture, and like objects were first removed. Wood was one of the important items salvaged. Rails and deck lumber were of excellent fir. Oak ceiling and panelling were recovered from each ship to the amount of three thousand and four thousand feet. Much of the panelling was of the tongue and groove variety and of high quality. It was removed intact and used in various construction jobs. Flooring was salvaged in large quantities. It also went into construction work. Wood came from many places on the ships; from masts, booms, bunks, drawers, and so forth. Planking two and a half to five inches thick served as cargo batten on the bottom of the boats. Hatch beams were taken off intact and used as platforms in construction work.

The wood removed from each ship averaged between eighty and ninety thousand feet. Scrap wood from the submarine type boats was carried as cargo in the lakers. Sawdust was utilized in many ways—it was soaked in oil and used in sweeping floors; it was used in the butcher shops of our commissaries; it was used in the tumblers; it was sent to pulverizers and mixed with coal for certain purposes. Twenty-five to thirty kegs of nails were sent to the electric furnaces each day and thirty-two or thirty-three pounds of steel derived from them. As many bolts and nuts as possible were salvaged and rethreaded; others were reduced to steel.

Three to four hundred pounds of paper were salvaged each day. This included not only waste paper but beaverboard and other paper combinations used in ship construction. All paper went to the company's paper mill, where it was reclaimed. Radiators were removed intact, reconditioned, and used in new buildings. Molding was saved as such when in good condition.

Hardware was removed in large quantities—hinges, locks, and door knobs were all reconditioned and sent to stock. All brass fasteners were saved; those that could be were preserved in their original form; others were reduced to metal. Mirrors that were in good shape were used in buildings; defective ones were sent to the glass plant and used as cullet in the production of new glass. Cabin windows of standard size were saved and used in construction work; all other glass including porthole windows and picture frames was remelted as cullet.

Electricians removed all electrical fixtures. Navigation instruments were saved whenever found. Engine-room control systems were saved intact. Forty to fifty steam and oil gauges were salvaged from each ship; they were reconditioned and sent to stock. Pumps of different sizes and purposes were recovered in large numbers. Steam injectors and ejectors were salvaged. Ice machines were saved as such. Globes, lights, wash basins, and lanterns all went to stock for future use; coffee urns, galley stoves, and kitchen utensils were used in small quantities at the company's lumber camps; some scales were reconditioned and used in the commissaries; eight meat-chopping blocks were used in the commissaries; signal flags were cleaned and the cloth used for different purposes.

Cork taken from ice boxes and in small quantities from the crews' quarters was preserved and put to various uses; much of it was sent to the Iron Mountain plant, where it was used as dry-kiln insulation. Asbestos was cut from the pipes and boilers. It was sent to a special asbestos plant, where it was ground and molded into new blocks. Oil recovered from the engine-room fuel-oil tanks and the storm-oil tanks was sent to the oil-salvage department and reclaimed. Paint was found in many ships' store rooms. It was reclaimed.

Bracket steps on the smoke stacks were used as fire ladders. Porthole lids were remelted for their brass. Steering wheels were stored. The brass sprocket chains, cams, and pulleys of the steering apparatus were all preserved and put to different uses. Steel cable that was in good condition was saved intact. Frayed cable was remelted. Towing hawsers were put to various uses. Those in good shape were saved intact; others were unravelled to make twine; still others were chopped up for use as seat-cushion packing.

All pipe was removed without cutting and sent to a special pipe-salvage department for reclaiming. Masts were burned off at the deck line, the rivets cut out, the wood parts dismantled, and the outer shells rolled into sheet steel. Winches and windlasses were removed and sent to storage.

One hundred and seventy-eight men were employed at the wood dock, not including those engaged in the removing of pipe and electrical fixtures. They stripped a ship of everything and moved readily. By the time a vessel was ready to be moved to its place on the main dismantling dock it had been fairly well cleared to the hull.

In the first operation all the upper parts of the hull and the steel decks were cut out by torches and lifted to the dock. Then the vessel was moved along in to the "big hook." Although the main engine weighed approximately seventy-five tons and the boilers more than fifty tons each, it took only an hour and a half to remove them. The crane not only lifted them from the boats but swung them in a 180 degree arc to the flat cars, which conveyed them to the storage ground. Many of the lakers carried engines and boilers from the submarine vessels rather than scrap steel as cargo.

With the power plant out, a vessel was moved back once more to its original position. It now resembled a huge canoe with its gaunt sides and empty interior. Torch and crane stripped the side plates into ribbons. The bow, with its heavy supports and reinforcements, presented a difficult problem. These had to be cut through before it was removed.

The shaft-tunnel casing was cut away by torch, but the propeller shaft was removed in sections by merely uncoupling the flanges. Lower blades on most of the propellers had been cut away before the vessels started the trip to the Rouge plant, so that they would not serve as a drag in the water. What remained of the propeller was lifted out whole. The rudder post was cut through at the bottom; at the top two small sections of plate were left fast to the post for facility in handling. The side plates were cut down to approximately three feet above the water line.

With a ship stripped virtually to the tank top, it took its last water journey. It was towed a few feet to the floating dry dock, where the double bottom was lifted clear of the water. Most of the double-bottom sections were lined with concrete, a precaution taken when the ships were built to protect the metal from such water as would accumulate in the hold. It was necessary to remove this concrete where the cutting was to be done. Small sections of plate were cut from the tank top across the beam of the ship just large enough for men with pneumatic drills to be able to chip out the concrete in three-inch channels.

Burners followed these men, and cut the double bottom into sections approximately six feet wide. The length of the sections varied according to the part of the ship they were taken from, the bow and the stern naturally being smaller than the midship portions. The length of the midship sections was about forty-three feet, six inches. After being cut the double-bottom sections were lifted from the dry dock, loaded three deep on flat cars, and taken to the storage yard, where they awaited their turn at the open-hearth furnaces.

In those double bottoms where oil had accumulated, notably in ships of the submarine type, additional difficulties were encountered. No matter how thoroughly the

Q

double-bottom tanks were pumped, a heavy coating of oil would remain over the whole inside surface, and use of the torch would inevitably result in a disastrous fire. This necessitated first cleaning these double bottoms by a patented process, a slow and expensive undertaking. Oil thus removed, however, was salvaged.

Large quantities of clean steel were salvaged from the ships, clean steel being that which could be used direct in construction and other work without being put through the furnaces. This was unloaded onto the main dock, where a crew of men with pneumatic air guns knocked off the rivets. The clean steel was then sent to a special stockyard. The rivets and broken bolts were melted for their metal. Other steel was loaded on flat cars from the ships and taken immediately to the storage yards.

Thus we secured a large collection of many kinds of engines and a fine lot of the best steel in addition to an immense collection of miscellaneous parts and materials. The disposition of some of these has already been noted.

We did not consider that steel that we took from the ships as scrap unless we could find no other uses for it. Scrapping and remelting is a last resort, for that means abandoning a considerable part of the labour that has already gone into the making of the piece and starting the material through another cycle of manufacturing. Our thought was to preserve in so far as possible the labour which the ships represented.

On an average we found from three to four hundred tons of clean steel in each ship. The shell plating, the deck plating, the ceilings, the smokestacks, the bulkheads, and the superstructure each contributed a quota.

We found all kinds of uses for these plates and shapes. For instance, we used strong backs from the hatches as I-beams for balconies. Rudder plates were used as liners in gondola type railway cars. Ship plate was used in the construction of coke-oven chutes. Machine steel from boat davits, steering gear, and so forth, was re-rolled and put to various uses. Ship steel was used almost exclusively in rebuilding ten of the boats as lake barges. Sections of tail shafts were annealed, tested, and then heated and forged to stock. Metal thus reclaimed was of exceptionally high quality and was used for tool steel.

Not a great deal of the steel could go directly into the fabrication of cars, for each part of a car has a special steel of its own, but such of the steel plate as was of the proper composition for car parts we rolled to the necessary thickness and then stamped or forged into car parts. Such of the steel as was not in condition to be used as it stood was treated as scrap and of this we sent from thirty-five to forty-five carloads a day to our furnaces. This was as much as the furnace could handle, but it fell far short of the daily dismantling output, and we accumulated immense quantities in storage—enough probably to meet our needs for this kind of steel for several years to come. Much of this stored steel is made up from the keel sections that were cut by torches from the ship in the final operation of dismantling on the floating dry dock. These sections weigh around six thousand pounds each, and their melting gave us a good deal of trouble, for the sections are big and awkward to handle, and breaking them up proved to be very expensive. Finally we found we could melt them most cheaply and most conveniently by simply lowering the sections end on into ladles of molten blast furnace metal, using three tons of ship metal to seventy-five tons of iron. In this fashion the big sections are being gradually, used up.

At our open-hearth furnaces we had to devise means for cutting the larger shapes down to charging-box size. We did this by putting in a steel hydraulic shear rated to give a pressure of one thousand tons. This we used for the big stock, and for the smaller stock we supplied other shears of various sizes adapted to the work. The cutting up of the big stock was rather interesting. It was unloaded from the flat cars by crane and magnet to a conveyor controlled from the operation station of the thousand-ton shear. The conveyor delivered the stock on the shear's V-shaped anvil. The stock was crushed with the wedge-shaped rear portion of the shear head. First the conveyor moved it forward until it projected over the forward edge of the anvil. Then the shear head descended, cutting the crushed stock away with its blade while the wedge-shaped rear portion simultaneously crushed the stock on the anvil. A discharge conveyor delivered the cut stock into charging boxes placed on two cars holding eight each. The cars were moved backward and forward beneath the edge of the conveyor by a control located in the conveyor operating station. A crane lifted four full boxes at a time and elevated them to the charging floor, placing them directly on cars that were hauled by electric locomotives, and filled their places with empty boxes.

We saved all of the engines, marine pumps, and the like, and also all the boilers. They all were intrinsically good, but since they had been made in a hurry for the war, little attention had been given to outside finish and appearance. It is our policy to have every tool and machine not only good but also good looking.

We could not recondition all the engines at once, but those which went into storage were thoroughly cleaned, painted, and guarded against deterioration.

An engine to be reconditioned was first completely dismantled; then, part by part, it was cleaned, fitted, tested, and reassembled to precision requirements greater even than when originally built. All bearings—crankshaft, main, and connecting rod—were scraped one by one, then sandpapered and refitted. The insides of cylinders were cleaned and sanded; cylinder-head covers and valve covers were cleaned and repacked; cylinders were lined up to the crankshaft. Crossheads to cylinders and crankshafts were lined up, as were water columns and slides. Pistons were overhauled and refitted. Valves were completely overhauled; valve stems were scraped and fitted to brackets; valve stem crosshead bearings were cleaned and fitted; valves and valve seats were cleaned and scraped. The throttle valve was cleaned and refitted completely.

To compensate for the loss of driveshaft and propeller, as originally installed in the ship, it was necessary in adapting a marine engine to land use to install a flywheel weighing about thirteen and one-half tons. A governor was also needed. Existing governors were found inadequate and outside experts consulted declared it would not be possible to design one without redesigning the engine. We designed a new governor capable of controlling the engine's uniformity of speed within one to one-and-a-half cycles at sixty cycles, when attached to a one thousand kilowatt generator.

As a safety precaution the entire frame of the engine was inclosed in a brass casing fitted with glass windows. This not only acted as a safety device but conserved heat and prevented dust and dirt from being admitted to moving parts.

Each reconditioned engine required a unit of two boilers. We used some of these about our plants, and still others have gone to various branches throughout the country, while others and also smaller engines taken from the ships have been sent to our shops in various parts of the world. The stairways and gratings have gone into our construction work. The searchlights are very useful as floodlights. The ice machines have been overhauled and adapted for cooling water in the plants. And so on through an enormous catalogue of uses.

All of these have been real uses. We have not simply rigged up things in order to use this stock, but in every case used it instead of buying something on the outside. All of which goes to illustrate the great advances that are possible in the standardizing of primary units. Factories used to be built solely to order, but now the erecting of a factory or an office building is largely a question of the arrangement of standard shapes and sizes of steel and other materials. The building of a ship has always been special. We have found through disassembling a ship that its parts fit very well into a building, and it is not at all impossible that putting together a steel ship and putting together a steel building have a great deal in common.

Has this work of disassembling paid? We bought the ships for $1,697,470. We spent about a million dollars in special equipment for the disassembling, but all of this equipment can be used for other purposes, so it cannot be charged entirely as an expense of the job. The total wages on the job ran to about half a million dollars and these, together with the supplies used, make the total cost of buying and dismantling well over three million dollars— provided all the machinery especially bought for the job is charged to it. We do not know the credit side of the job, and we shall never know. For on each part we should have to ascertain the cost of reconditioning and then find out how much it would cost to buy something for the same purpose on the outside—and that would be only playing a game of bookkeeping with ourselves. However, we have on the credit side something that cannot be reduced to figures—we have the experience which our men gained in solving this big new problem. That is always a prime profit. The training we gained, the confidence, the new insight into methods render me quite indifferent to anything that figures could show. In reckoning gains you must reckon the growing ability of your organization as far more important than a growing balance at the bank.

We already knew something about the secondary use of materials and supplies and a number of our experiments are described in *Today and Tomorrow*. We are now, as then, more interested in avoiding waste than in salvaging it. We try to have our materials and supplies reach us in such form that they will cut up with a minimum of waste, but as yet we must do some reclaiming. For instance, about seventy tons of special steels are consumed every day in the River Rouge plant in the maintenance and replacement of tools, dies, machine parts, and the like. All of this we now reclaim in special electric furnaces. As scrap this steel would bring very little and therefore it is worth saving. Lead is an expensive material and therefore we put in a department to recover the lead used in batteries. Likewise we have a department for salvaging rubber, and take out three grades. The first grade is used in manufacturing waterproof materials for tops and curtains; the second grade is for making hard-rubber parts; while the third grade furnishes insulating material.

We have an immense amount of scrap of various kinds every day, and all of it is utilized or sold. We have, for instance, five hundred tons of steel turning every day—or fifteen carloads—which are sold to various mills, the quantity being too great for any one mill to absorb. We have about ten carloads a day of trimmings from the sheet metal stamping operations and three carloads of drop forge flashings. These go back to our own furnaces. An Eastern optical firm takes the left-over cuttings from wool upholstery and makes them into polishers for eyeglasses. The insulators on the ammeters are made from cards such as are punched in the time clocks for the employees. And so on.

There is no economy in all this; we are simply following the doctrine of use. We are not trying to save things but to get the utmost use out of them. And, incidentally, one of the best ways to get the full use out of anything is always to keep it clean. Paint and light are great aids to constructive economy.

CHAPTER XVI

TAKING THE METHODS OVERSEAS

FOR many years we have been selling our products abroad. Model T has penetrated to every corner of the earth. But we have only sold—we have not until now done much manufacturing—abroad. The parts have largely been made in Detroit and then put together on the foreign assembly line. These assembly lines have done little or no manufacturing. The only exception is the British Isles, where our plants at Cork, Ireland, and Manchester, England, were together able to turn out a complete car.

In Europe we have been concerned entirely with putting our policies into effect, and complete ownership has hitherto been necessary because not otherwise could we control the direction. Now, however, conditions are sufficiently changed to warrant a change in policy if the company is to continue to give the largest service to the largest number of people.

Therefore we have now reorganized our companies in England, Germany, France, and other countries, recapitalized them on a very conservative basis, and have sold stock in each company to the citizens of the country in which it is situated. We retain the control of each company only so that it may be managed in accordance with our

fundamental principles and have the benefit of our engineering experience. We are not at all interested merely
in floating a number of automobile companies in Europe
or anywhere else in the world. But we believe that our industrial policies move toward the end of creating consuming power, raising the standards of living, and thus dimin-
ishing poverty. In this belief we may be right or again we
may be wrong—we believe that our experience has proved
that we are right.

We believe that the automobile is in itself, both directly
and indirectly, an important wealth-producing instrument,
provided that it can be made so cheaply and so well that
it can be put into the hands of the great mass of the population. It took the United States a long time to learn
that the low-priced automobile was not simply a luxury
that people would be better off without. We have seen
the buying of automobiles pass down gradually from the
higher ranges of wealth to a point where, by reason of
a secondhand car at fifty or twenty-five dollars, anyone
can own one. And we have seen the effects of this ownership on the prosperity of the country. The people of
the United States do not own automobiles because they
are prosperous. They are prosperous because they own
automobiles and use them as tools to increase the range of
their abilities.

That is one phase of the automobile, and it is peculiar
to the automobile, but also there is the manner of its
making that need not be peculiar to the automobile. It
will apply to any commodity, and this method has by common consent been taken as fundamental to America's pros-

perity. The genesis of the method and its development have
been explained at length in *My Life and Work* and in
Today and Tomorrow; its further development has been
explained in certain of its phases in the earlier chapters of
this book. All that we have done or are to-day doing is
open to the world to see. We have no secret processes and
no magic formulas, but while the principles and their application are gradually becoming understood and followed
in the United States they do not seem in every instance
to be comprehended by the peoples from overseas.

We have been visited by many hundreds of foreign dele-
gations, practically all of them searching for the secret
of quick wealth. Not finding it they go away wondering.
They seem not to comprehend the economy of the high
wage or its influence upon consumption. Whether they be
employers or whether they be workmen, the same thing is
true. They do not comprehend; they simply say that we
can do this or that because of the wealth inherent in the
home market of the United States. They do not see that
this is a *created* wealth, not merely a collected or accumulated wealth, and that our own company not many years
ago was as small as a company could be, and that we have
risen largely on the wealth that has been created through
our service. Of course a company such as our own could
not be built all at once simply by spending money. Ours
is a development and not a promotion. The time element
in our experience could not be duplicated for ten times our
capital. No one can start where we are now, but the underlying principles of our policies have nothing to do with
size. It is to demonstrate that prosperity can deliberately

be produced that we have planted our roots in foreign soils—not primarily for our own benefit but because we believe we have an industrial method of bringing more comfort and more opportunity to people in the old lands.

This is not for a moment to say that these foreign enterprises are undertaken in any spirit of charity. I firmly believe that the prosperity of the United States, as well as the peace of the world, is dependent on levelling up the state of the prosperity among the people of all nations. If our policy of lending large sums will result merely in the maintenance of an economic system that in the past has been unfavourable to popular prosperity and too favourable to war, it will not be of much benefit to the plain people of Europe. There must some day be an end to the cumulative borrowing. It seems, as I shall later explain, that the objectives of creating and sharing prosperity may be the more easily realized by taking in as partners the peoples of the countries in which we operate. That is the reason for the sales of stock in England, Germany, and France. In Russia we have necessarily pursued a different course. We are there erecting for the account of the Soviet government an automobile plant which they will own and manage. We are training men for them in our factories; we are turning over to them all our blueprints and plans and are undertaking to keep them informed of our technical progress. All this we are doing at cost. If we were simply selling our product we could do so at considerably less trouble than this, but we think that Russia needs modern industry and more particularly the automotive industry in order that the wealth of the country may be opened up.

Otherwise it will remain one of the sore spots of the world.

Likewise in Brazil we are endeavouring to establish a rubber industry, and for a number of reasons. The world's use of rubber is bound to increase so rapidly that no source of rubber now existing will be able to supply even a small part of the demand. The world has not yet really begun to appreciate the value of rubber. It is the best silencer that we know, and one of these days we shall have to attack the problem of noise, for, aside from everything else, a large part of the noises with which we are afflicted comes from unnecessary jars. These shorten the life of all kinds of machinery. How long would an automobile last running on steel rims? Rubber must be produced in greater quantities and as a very cheap commodity. The wise course is not to monopolize present trade in rubber but to prepare for the greatly increased demand for rubber soon to be made.

In none of these foreign operations has there been any effort to gain concessions or privileges or otherwise to obtain a preferred position. We wish to start on an equal footing with other industry in the same country.

The foreign enterprises in which we are engaged have been the subject of occasional foreign criticism and will undoubtedly be the subject of further criticism until they have been operating for some years. The criticism runs in various directions. Some of it has to do with the professed fear of an American invasion growing out of the old thought that business must be envisaged in terms of conquest. Then there is the notion that we are devotees of a standardization to the end of making all things and all peoples quite alike and eventually making man himself a machine product. And finally the raising of wages is viewed with great alarm as tending to upset the traditional relation between the rich and the poor.

Let me say at once that the idea of invasion and conquest is not part of the thought of a normally developing business. A great many European firms do business—and a very good business too—in the United States, and I am sure that no American business man thinks of their presence here in terms of an attempted invasion and conquest. They are welcome. We invite them. Many American business men regret that our tariff arrangements seem to justify the impression that we oppose the business enterprise of other nations coming into the American market. Every business man worth his salt knows that the more business men you have in a market the more business you have. So when American business in turn goes to Europe I cannot see why it should be considered as an alien and hostile invasion. Certainly it is not alien. Those who carry business back to Europe are the men, or their sons, whom Europe gave to America. It is more like a home-coming than an invasion. Why should Europe fear to receive again the initiative and enterprise she herself planted here?

Now as to the fear of what is called "American standardization," I quite understand it; we should all fear it if it were anything like the notion of it which haunts the European mind. It is very doubtful if the European who visits America ever sees the thing that he fears. It is not life that is standardized; it is rather that the standards of the goods and the services that minister to life have been raised to a higher level than formerly. If American stand-

ardization meant that everything was to be cut to the
same pattern, it would have destroyed itself long ago. Versatility is not believed to have departed from Americans
even by their critics. However, it is quite futile ever to hope
to dispel the fear of standardization by mere words. We
can only ask the fearful to reflect that standards can mean
something besides sameness, and then we must trust the
principle itself to make its way.

Another thing which we find as a result of what is called
the "industrial invasion" of Europe is the fear that the
American invader will succeed in turning everyone into a
factory hand. This is probably the most pathetic of all the
misconceptions of the function of industry. Everyone at
work and everyone prosperous does not mean everyone in
a factory. They have had practically a factory civilization
in Europe for generations without much prosperity. Industry, creating and sharing proper wages, is the strongest
force we know in dwarfing the factory by stimulating the
rise of all the other institutions natural to a modern progressive community. It requires a comparatively small
number of the population, remuneratively employed in industry, to give an impetus to all other lines at the same
time. In an industrial civilization you have something more
than smokestacks—you have first of all respectable homes,
large numbers of them, and then all the other forms of
commercial and cultural life which mark the most advanced peoples. The industrial factory becomes not the
immediate scene of all the people's labours but the power
house of economic energy for the community at large.

The system of industry to which I am committed takes

for granted that poverty is a curable illness, and that the cure lies in so arranging industrial production that through high wages, which by the application of engineering skill become low wages per unit of production, the power of consumption will steadily be raised until poverty will become practically a voluntary matter having to do with the willingness to work. Under such conditions the very small percentage of any population who cannot work in productive enterprise can easily be cared for.

Centuries ago the pioneers came out from Great Britain and the Continent into a new world, and there they found wealth by developing a continent. On that new continent were born new ideas. I view American business going into Europe as simply a returning to the mother soil of these new ideas. The ideas that came from the Old World to the New World were remade in the New World in better fashion. I think that the ideas now going from the New World back to the Old World will there undergo another transformation, become yet more powerful, and result in an ultimate interchange of the best ideas of several civilizations and a better general result than could be achieved by either the Old World or the New World acting alone. For each has things that the other lacks.

We know that high wages, which result in high production to take care of high consumption generated by the high wages, form the best equipment with which to attack poverty. As we go forward we shall learn more.

Substituting the engineer for the politician is a very natural step forward. The engineer can do that which the politician cannot do under any circumstances. The engi-

R

neer creates and harmonizes while the politician can at the best only rearrange what he has in hand. A good engineer is not a standardizer in any objectionable sense. The robot, for instance, is merely the creation of a wholly misinformed literary imagination and is really a childish sort of conception. It grows out of the thought that machinery is labour saving instead of labour serving, and that the end of machinery is to eliminate men—whereas its only function is to produce for men.

One may have an engineering mind without being an engineer. And also one may be an engineer without having an engineering mind. The true engineering mind views machinery not as a thing of itself but as a means to an end.

The prejudice against engineers as being those who would standardize the world is as ill conceived as would be a similar prejudice against biologists. No one who knows anything about life ever thinks of standardizing it. However, the best machine is an affair of easements and allowances bound up in a body of definite purpose and precise relationships. And who doubts that if human society were more like that, freedom would be increased in the world and distress lessened?

Engineering spells freedom. Men were held to a single spot before the engineer came. By steam and motor car and airplane he has liberated man. He has lengthened man's day with light, increased the limits of man's life through food and sanitation, emancipated man's mind, and given him a sense of possible mastery over elements and environment—in short, the engineer found society immobile and left it mobile. Yet he is now charged by bookish people with wanting to fix the world in a rigid casting!

The American industrial and economic thought differs widely from that of the rest of the world. If America is of any value to the world, it is because America is American. And America's value cannot be increased by making her anything else.

We should not overlook the fact that America's value to the world consists not in the money it may lend but in its being a demonstration and a challenge. We have demonstrated, against many prophecies of failure, that the people who founded this country and whose descendants hold it, are capable of self-rule. We have demonstrated that for all practical purposes there are always being thrown up from the midst of the people men who can meet the times and make way for the future. We have demonstrated, as Great Britain has in spite of systems that may seem to say the opposite, that nobility is, if anything, a national and not merely a family asset.

CHAPTER XVII

THE WORK ABROAD

THE statement is often made that the American is a greenhorn in foreign business, but it is doubtful if anyone has ever known very much about foreign business. This is only part and parcel of the ignorance of business in general. The state which foreign business gets itself into every little while, its failure to knit bonds of peace between peoples, as well as its long reputation as a money loser, is evidence enough that foreign or export business is far from being a science or even a fairly profitable art. But when all is said and done, this ignorance popularly attributed to Americans concerning the doing of business abroad may not be so regrettable, for it is pretty hard to learn something that is not right. It is a question whether foreign business up to this time has much, if any, principle or method that could be learned.

Whatever until now the general lack of knowledge in this direction has been, there is no doubt that events are quite actively correcting that defect. To-day we are nearer the truth about expansion of business into foreign fields than we have been at any time during the industrial era. Previous to the industrial era, foreign business was on a natural basis. Customers went to foreign lands, or sent their agents, to buy what those lands afforded—spices, silks, and all the romantic commodities of early commerce. People sent for what they wanted to where they could get it. It was a trade not based on commercial enterprise but on merit and use. True, the volume was not large, but the system was natural. There was no artificial stimulus behind it. It was ability to buy searching for ability to make and sell. It was not the energetic outpushing of manufacturing peoples to capture world markets. Briefly, it was buying, not selling.

It would not be entirely pleasant to recount what foreign trade has become in the meantime. But we are now arriving at some very definite views of what foreign trade should be and what it is likely to become. For one thing, we are recognizing the folly of expecting that any nation will continue indefinitely to be a market for another nation. The effect of American trade in many foreign lands has been to stimulate them to self-supply. Their very experience with our machinery has had the effect of inspiring them with industrial aspirations of their own. Any scheme of foreign business built upon the theory that foreign countries will forever, or even long, remain dependents on American industry is likely to prove disappointing. It may well be that by reason of racial skill or natural resources one nation may always retain its position to serve others in certain respects—that is, keep other nations always in a customer status with reference to certain products—but the cases will be exceptional in so far as industry is concerned. Many exponents of foreign business have assumed that the American workingman was going to be the factory hand for the whole world:

that America was to be the factory, and the rest of the nations our dressed-up customers. This view was supported by another assumption, namely, that foreign business brains could not compete with ours, that foreign workmen were not as competent as ours, and so on through the whole gamut of boastful ignorance. As to foreign business brains, they are the same as ours, and as to foreign workingmen it has been the experience of the Ford Motor Company in its European shops that, given the same relative wages and working conditions, the European workman is not at all inferior to the American. Of course, the alleged inferiority is there, but it is not essentially in the men, it is in their wages and working conditions. There should be no difficulty in accepting these facts, since Europe and the United States are made up of the same kind of people.

Our company has had a measure of success in foreign business based on two principles: first, taking to the nations a commodity that they needed and the use of which assisted them to develop their own affairs, and second, an absolute renunciation of every form of exploitation. That is, our purpose was not to make American business greater at the expense of other nations, but to help make other peoples more prosperous by the aid of American business. There can be no other abiding basis for foreign business by any company or any country. And even then there will be no abiding relationship of seller and buyer between nations. International exchange of goods will always exist, of course, but not always of the same goods or in the same quantities. One great effect of American business abroad may be to teach our foreign customers how to supply themselves with the goods they now buy from us. Undoubtedly many countries now more or less dependent on industrial countries for supply will themselves become sufficiently industrial to supply their own requirements. That is, in commercial language, we will lose the market. But that is all to the good. As progressive beings we should look forward with approval to the time when new nations or backward nations shall outgrow their dependence and feel little or no further need for us. At that time international trade will then settle to the natural basis of need and supply, each nation supplying others with that commodity which it is most fitted to produce. This outlook is probably little relished by the heated salesmanship of the times, but it seems to be what is coming.

Russia came to us and asked assistance toward planting the automobile industry in that country, and although we shall have no authority or interest in the industry that will be established there, we readily consented on the principle that it is never wrong to help people to get to work and that the automobile is an instrument of social prosperity.

Our other activities outside the United States were formerly all operated under our sole ownership, but with the development of industrial effort abroad we have felt that our factories ought to belong in part to the people of the countries amongst whom we were doing business. After consideration of all that was involved, and feeling that if we know what is right to do nothing remains but to do it, we began the organization of our business abroad on a partnership basis, starting with the Ford Motor Company of England. I am glad to say that European industrialists have welcomed a complete demonstration of our principles in the various countries, and although it is not always at first clear to them how they can fully approve our rate of wages, yet there is no doubt in my mind that the desire to improve the lot of Europe's workingmen is so strong in progressive European industrialists that a way to better wages will be found. It is one thing to criticize the European industrialist and another thing to understand his problems, but I am sure that industrial leadership in Europe will bring about much social betterment there without mere imitation of American ways. They are too wise to be mere imitators of us, for then they would have to take our defects, too, which is not desirable.

It meant not a thing to us whether we owned or did not own the whole of the British company. But it does mean something to a country whether a concern is a foreign concern or one having a stake in the country. Our interest was in doing a job, and if that job could be better alone by selling stock, then we would sell stock—provided that we were not put in the position of promoting a company or paying bankers to get money for us that we did not want. Therefore, having made it very plain why we were offering stock, we reorganized the Ford Motor Company, Ltd., with a capitalization of seven million pounds divided into shares of one pound each and offered forty per cent of this for public subscription in England. We desired as far as possible to keep the shares out of speculative hands,

to allot in small shares, and not to allot to American investors. The issue was not underwritten and there were no bankers' profits of any kind. We simply offered the stock for sale at par. It was very heavily oversubscribed and, although a portion of the stock undoubtedly got into the hands of speculators, the majority reached the British investors for whom it was intended.

The company had already taken over the Manchester plant of the former Ford Motor Company, Ltd., and this will be retained as an assembly plant; the company had also bought three hundred and six acres at Dagenham, which is about eighteen miles east of London. On May 16, 1929, ground was here broken for a plant that will in the beginning be capable of producing one thousand cars a day and employ about fifteen thousand men. Later we believe that this capacity will be doubled. This company has taken over Henry Ford & Son, Ltd., at Cork, and also our various companies on the Continent, and will manufacture, assemble, distribute, and market for Great Britain, Ireland, and all of the Continent except Soviet Russia. It will be the largest automobile company outside of the United States. We have not gone into the matter in a small way—except of course as compared with our operations in the United States.

We picked out the Dagenham site because it has water, rail, and motor transport, and we can therefore put into it everything that we have learned at the River Rouge about the economical handling of materials. The property has a frontage on the River Thames. On this we are building a jetty equipped with railroad tracks and cranes, and we

are also building a high line on the same general plans as
that at the River Rouge. That is, we have an elevated
structure extending over all the storage bins and connecting with all parts of the works and furnished with
travelling cranes and railroad tracks, in order that no
materials, supplies, or finished parts will have to be
trucked or touched by hand. The London, Midland &
Scottish Railways runs through the north end of the property, while the Southend Road also touches the property
and gives easy access to London by motor.

River boats, large or small, may dock at the wharf and
transfer their cargoes directly to any part of the plant.
Most of our ore, coal, and sandstone will arrive by water,
and by means of the high line the cargoes, without any
handling at all, will be shifted to storage bins. The materials arriving by rail can be handled likewise. The property has ore and coal fairly close at hand, and, with the
transport arrangements, the savings in freight alone will
be considerable.

The power plant at the beginning will have a capacity
of thirty thousand kilowatts and will be unusual in that
its principal fuel will be the refuse of London, which for
hundreds of years has been burning on the dumps near by.
When, on my visit to London, I saw these burning dumps,
it occurred to me that they might as well burn to some
purpose and that purpose could be the generating of steam.
Hence we have devised plans to burn all of this refuse and
our tests show that from 666 tons of refuse burned a day
we can get 210,000 pounds of steam per hour. This refuse,
which will arrive by boat at the jetty, will be handled on

an endless conveyor from the jetty to the power house
or to a storage bin when the supply exceeds our need.

The manufacturing buildings will follow our standard
American style, but are being built by British contractors
with British labour and materials. In fact, the more employment we can create in Britain the better we are
pleased. All of the machinery is being built in England
according to our designs, and of course all of the arrangements and the like will exactly follow our home practices.

And also following our home practices we shall manufacture something of everything that goes to make up a
finished car, but, as at home, our principal business will be
motor making. We shall make all of our own motors, but
as for the rest of the car we shall contract from the outside
for most of our needs and shall probably have hundreds
of companies throughout the United Kingdom manufacturing parts according to our designs and as far as possible according to our plans. We intend to sell the finished
cars at prices approximating those in the United States
(except for government charges added). We even hope
that the English company will be able to sell for less than
the American company. The parts bought on the outside
will have to be produced economically. They can be so
produced only through the use of well-designed machinery
of the labour-serving character attended by men who receive high wages. High-class, low-priced goods cannot be
produced by obsolete methods.

We are providing for two batteries of eighty-eight coke
ovens each of the by-product type, and the output of these

ovens will, for the time being, be sufficient for the blast furnaces and the foundry, while the gas generated will be used in the various manufacturing processes of the plant just as at the River Rouge. We shall sell the by-products such as tar, ammonium sulphate, benzol, and so forth, in the market. The gas from the furnaces will, as at Dearborn, be burned under the steam boilers, and we have laid out the foundry and the furnaces so as to follow our American practice of casting directly from the hot furnace metal so as to avoid the expense of reheating.

In fact, our experiences at the River Rouge are permitting us to get even more economical plant transportation in England than we have in America. We are arranging, as usual, completely to reclaim or salvage all used materials and, in fact, to do everything in this British plant that has been developed out of our experience in our American plants.

The manufacturing policies of this plant will be precisely the same as in the United States. We shall have exactly the same kind of machinery as we have at home, and the improvements that we daily make at Dearborn will be communicated at once to Dagenham, while improvements made at Dagenham will be communicated to the United States. All our information will be interchangeable, and we expect to get as much as we give.

Of course we shall not use a single man more than is necessary to use, for otherwise the public could not get the benefit of labour-serving machinery in lower prices, nor could the men get it in higher wages. But we shall need

the skill of the British or Scottish machinists in our tool rooms, and we shall need every kind of skill in our manufacturing operations, and this will afford an opportunity for the hiring of many men whose trades have crumbled beneath them—as, for instance, the coal miners who have for so long been out of work and have no skill that fits into any other part of the British industrial organization. We shall pay a minimum wage of one pound a day as we have always done in England and the men will work eight hours a day.

If the experiment is to mean anything, then the policies have to be completely carried out.

The same policy that has been inaugurated in Great Britain is being followed with our companies on the continent of Europe, but on somewhat smaller scales. We want to manufacture as much as possible of a car in the country where it is assembled and sold, in order to generate the largest possible amount of purchasing power through the payment of high wages.

There is a leaven of our industrial methods working everywhere in Europe to-day because of the fact that we have to be supplied with parts after our design by factories in Denmark, France, Belgium, Germany, Japan, Spain, Italy, and Sweden. They are supplying us in parts with frames, front axles, fenders, hoods, running boards, radiators, starting motors, generators, coil units, head and tail lamps, tires, wheels, wire, glass, upholstering cotton, body cloth, artificial leather, and so on through quite a long list. All these are being made as well and as cheaply as we can make them and, of course, exactly according to our specifications and the methods which we have been able to recommend.

In Germany we recapitalized our company and intended to offer forty per cent of the shares to the public, but instead we sold the entire block to the I. G. Farbenindustrie —which is a combination of several great chemical and other industries and which has very largely adopted American methods in the conduct of its plants. Since the stock of this company is almost wholly held by Germans, the direct sale insured that our stock would be kept out of the speculative market. There is also a relation between the products made by this company and by our own company. Farben is the leader in the manufacture of light metal alloys, which are as hard as steel and weigh less, is very advanced in the manufacture of artificial leather and is the leader in the field of synthetic gasoline. The same policy of reorganizing the corporation and selling stock locally has been followed in Holland, Belgium, and France.

In Brazil we are pushing forward another enterprise, the fruits of which will not be evident for some years to come. We are of course established in a number of places in South America. We have assembly plants at Buenos Aires; at Lima, Peru; at Montevideo, Uruguay; at São Paulo and Pernambuco, Brazil; and at Santiago, Chile. But we have done no manufacturing at any of these plants, although whenever a local man can make a part satisfactorily we give him a contract.

The Brazilian project has to do with providing a sufficient supply of rubber in case that at some time in the future rubber from the Far East should not be available. As the world gains in its knowledge of the uses of rubber I am looking forward to a need for much larger quantities than are now produced. It takes some years for a rubber tree to come into bearing and, although now the capacity of the world to produce rubber is in excess of the demand for it, that condition will not long remain. The very existence of a surplus develops more uses for a product.

Para rubber is the best in the world and Brazil, as everyone knows, was once the supreme source of Para rubber. It is not at all outside the probabilities that Brazil will regain her importance in the world of rubber by the proper development of her rich natural advantages. Brazil needs only to know that the effort is for development and not for exploitation to render honest capital every necessary aid.

We have undertaken the cultivating of rubber on a large scale on a twenty-five hundred square mile stretch of territory on the Tapajoz River, which is a tributary of the Amazon. It is our thought that the principles of machine cultivation can be applied to rubber growing and that it need not be, as it now is, a hand operation. And also we believe the rubber may be manufactured where it is grown and that thereby a real industry may be created with an interchange of men between the plantations and the factory. As is usual with any new thing we undertake, we are slowly and carefully feeling our way. This is an enterprise of the future rather than of the present. But even in the present there is visible that without which no enterprise is satisfactory: there is a visible benefit already accruing to the people of the region which presages what prosperity awaits the people of Brazil.

We are, in every instance, trying to maintain in our foreign industries wages comparable to those paid in the United States. We do not base these wages at all on the cost of living but merely use the cost of living in any country to compare with the costs in the United States in order to arrange wages everywhere of equal buying power. The progress on this point is set out in a report of the managing director of the British company:

Almost everyone interested in the economies of industry is aware of the Ford theory (and practice) of high wages. For example, the average wage paid at our Manchester works (2,670 men) is 2s. 9¾d. per hour, and at Cork (6,705 men) 2s. 3¼d. per hour. We work only a 40-hour week. Wages paid in Ford factories throughout Europe are, having regard to variations in the cost of living, in proportion. I would like strongly to emphasize that these working hours and wages do not evidence any sort of haphazard experiment or diluted philanthropy. They are the result of very careful study and practical application over a long period of time, in many countries, with all sorts and conditions of men working amid varying social, climatic, and economic circumstances. The only constant factor is the class of work and the industrial and factory conditions. At a time when an eight-hour day was spoken of with bated breath—even by Labour leaders and social reformers—and when the earning of uniform and minimum wages sufficient to maintain self-respect and independence was considered to be an impossible ideal, Mr. Henry Ford had learned by practical experience and observation that high wages, short hours, and comfortable working conditions were the very best and most remunerative investment which capital could make.

The balance-sheet and accounts which we have before us to-day are practical demonstrations of this paramount industrial axiom.

The Ford car is essentially the same vehicle wherever it is manufactured or assembled. This uniformity of product affords us almost unique opportunity to make comparison. Similar tools and machinery and the same methods of manufacturing and assembly are employed in every Ford factory throughout the world. By watching and comparing results we discover and accumulate some most interesting data.

For example, so as to avoid the nuisance and complications of money currencies, we have initiated a labour currency. Factory experts call it "Minute Costs!" This company and its associated companies are employing Englishmen, Irishmen, Dutchmen, Frenchmen, Belgians, Danes, Germans, Italians, Spaniards, Swedes, Finns, and Turks, all working in their respective countries, and doing the same job with similar tools under equal factory conditions. We compare how long it takes each respective man to complete his work. In Denmark, where we pay the highest wages in Europe, we find the lowest minute costs. On the other hand, in Belgium, where the wages are lowest, the minute costs are highest. This is no flash-in-the-pan casual comparison. Week after week and month after month the figures confirm this experience.

What is probably more significant, during our task of relating and adjusting the wage rates so as to secure the uniformity I have referred to, we found it necessary substantially to increase the minimum wages at the Antwerp factory. The response of the worker was almost immediately displayed by a reduction of minute costs.

Last, but not least, I know you will be interested to hear that these comparative statistics have enabled us to establish the fact that the American workman is no miracle monger. Neither is the British, Irish, or Continental artisan any inferior creature. Given like conditions and treatment, our workers here in Europe actually beat their American cousins, as proved by the standard of our minute costs.

CHAPTER XVIII

EDUCATION FOR LEADERSHIP

FOR some years now I have been working out a system of education to the end of having pupils use their eyes really to see with, so that their brains may make use of what they see and thus give the opportunity for thinking from things instead of from words. This, it seems to me, will shorten the processes of thought. For, if one be thinking about things, then a quicker, clearer, and more accurate base for thinking can be had by seeing the actual thing than by merely reading about or even looking at a picture of the thing.

Then by having the thing itself in mind—instead of a more or less inaccurate impression of it—the mind will have the chance to work forward more precisely, for then at least one possibility of error will be removed. Now if, in addition, one can actually work not only with that thing but also with all the steps leading up to its development, then the brain has a still broader base of fact to work from. If the same process can be followed with a large number of things, then the brain will have a still broader base and a very great deal of time can be saved. There will be no need of speculating about that which has already been accomplished and the mind can go forward to speculating about that which has never been done.

In other words, it ought to be possible to short-cut the road to invention. For instance, if a man be working on electric motors, he will save years of research if he has at hand the actual examples of what everyone previously has done in electric motors. He can comprehend in a few hours or days what might otherwise take him years to learn.

This is the underlying thought of the whole plan that we are engaged in working out. The objective is to find and to equip boys who will develop into industrial leaders of men. By this I mean leaders who, by reason of ability in invention or in organization, will create new methods or remake old methods to provide more and more useful goods and therefore useful work for men everywhere. We have an ideal of education directed toward this end and one of the results of it may be a few real industrial leaders who will be able to do the best for the many men who are content merely to follow in the footsteps of others. As affairs now are, there is too much delay in finding our leaders; they emerge too late. I think that the process of equipping can be shortened and the process of real experience begun earlier. This is not to say that any plan of education will of itself produce leaders, but it seems possible to devise a method by which leaders may be recognized as they appear. The whole system of training that we are planning has this single end in view.

The system is not fixed and irrevocable. It will be changed as we learn from experience. The first to be educated are those who think about education. In fact, the only point that is absolutely and definitely known to us now is that the methods will constantly change—for otherwise we might be educating for a world that did not exist. And also our plans are not intended to take the place of other forms of education—although we hope to find some ideas that may prove to be of universal application. We do not pretend that educating for industrial leadership should be the end of all education. We are concerned solely with the job in hand, which to us seems to be the most important job that we can undertake. Whether or not it seems of like importance to someone else is of no consequence. It is our own task and we are trying to do it in our own way. That cannot be made too clear.

The plan as it now exists is extensive and, although a good deal has already been accomplished, it represents only a small fraction of what in the future we hope to accomplish. The fountainhead is the Edison Institute of Technology and the Greenfield Village at Dearborn— both of which are in partial operation and are nearing completion. These are tied up with our industries for the single reason that our operations at Dearborn provide a larger opportunity for experience in more fields of activity than could be had if they were academically isolated. To this Institute will come boys and young men who have demonstrated their possibilities of leadership in what might be called our feeder schools. We shall not restrict ourselves to these schools. We want the material of leadership wherever and however it may be found. Thirty-five boys are already at work in the Institute.

The schools already established and in operation are the so-called trade schools in our Highland Park and

River Rouge plants. These have in them some two thousand pupils. Our school at the Wayside Inn at South Sud-
bury, Massachusetts, contains some fifty pupils. We also
have a little school for younger boys and girls which holds
its sessions in the old schoolhouse that I attended myself
in Dearborn and which has been removed to Greenfield
Village and restored to its original condition. Throughout the country are other school sites where other schools
leading to Dearborn will be established, and gradually the
system will be extended until, as we hope, it will be able
to take care of at least a million children. We employ
throughout the world about two hundred thousand men
and take it therefore as an obligation of our industry to
provide facilities for the children of about that number
of families—that is to say, for about a million children.

It would be worse than idle to prophesy how many
leaders of men we shall get out of the large group of
boys who eventually will be gathered together. We may
get a great many, or again we may get none, and it
would not be fair to the students if only those with the
qualities of leadership could gain any benefit out of the
organization. Our plans, however, are not so selectively
exclusive. The first and most elemental feature of our
idea has to do with making every pupil self-supporting
from the moment that he enters the system. In supporting
themselves, they also pay the way of the institution. No
charity is anywhere involved, for by the very simple process of having the students do useful instead of useless
work in school it is possible for them to earn satisfactory
incomes during their school years, gain the habit of self-

reliance, and be wholly competent to earn their own livings anywhere in the outside world—if they do not happen to be chosen for further development. That is, our endowment is the energy of the student plus the experience of the educator.

I take it as a matter of course that a good citizen is one who, in addition to other qualities, has the training and ability to earn his own living anywhere at any time. That, at the very least, we already give to all of our pupils. Every man ought to have a trade of some kind and preferably a number of trades, so that, regardless of whatever form of work he may choose to do, he may always have something to fall back on in an emergency. And if a man aspires to be a leader, he must know a great deal about a great many trades. No man is going to do well in any line if he is haunted by the fear of poverty. A man with the ability to use his hands need never worry about his daily bread. A great deal of fine, constructive work is halted because the man capable of doing it never has his mind free to work. My idea of earning a living is that the living is a by-product. The provision of ordinary daily needs can and ought to be a mere detail of life and not life itself. One of the reasons why we have so much youthful crime is that boys are not taught from the very beginning to earn their own livelihoods—it is a detail they have not been helped to master. They try to get by foul means what they could much more easily get by fair means. The criminal works harder and gets less than the mechanic.

Why should we use the word "education" to describe

a course of study that fills a boy full of a lot of things that are useless, while never teaching him to use his eyes or to think for himself? What do I mean by useless ideas? Ideas that are not fruitful in experience and understanding and service. Of course, we all understand what is claimed for the mental gymnastic exercise of admittedly useless studies. But why not the mental gymnastics and the useful acquisitions at the same time? It may seldom require a change of subjects, but only another method of approach. History, for example: how different is the modern teaching of history from the methods used when we were young. We have history in our schools, but it is the history of evolving the mastery of the means of life.

In the Edison School of Technology we are trying to stimulate boys to think for themselves by working out practical problems and doing practical work, and their principal books will be the basic things—the materials and forces of Nature and human society—the machines, appliances, and tools that they see about them, and we hope that with so much of Mr. Edison's life before them they will fall into the spirit of independent invention and discovery.

They will have before them one or more of every tool and article that has been used in the United States from the earliest time down to the present, in addition they will have a complete series of all the devices which man has ever used for artificial lighting, and finally they will have authentic examples of every form in which motion has ever been transmitted by man. Therefore, if a boy be given a problem to solve, he will be able to see for himself how

others in the past have approached his problem, and if
no one before has ever had his exact problem, then he
will at least gain some very good suggestions of combinations that might be made. And possibly out of these
combinations he will devise something entirely original.

The collection of objects which have already been made
comprises hundreds of thousands of pieces and the mere
putting of these in order will require years of the most
useful possible work on the part of the advanced pupils
in the Institute. This is in the way of learning the A B C's
of industry by learning to work from the ground up as
the earlier men did. We have the original machine shop
that Mr. Edison used at Menlo Park and it is fitted with
the same kind of machinery that he had in it—in some
cases we have the very machines—and the atmosphere of
this shop we hope will not only be a spur to achievement
but also give a more fundamental knowledge of accurate
hand work than would be otherwise possible. We shall
shortly have another machine shop fitted up in the style
and with the tools of old New England so that the boys
will accustom themselves to another kind of equipment
and atmosphere.

For each division of work we have an old and highly
skilled worker. He works with and directs the boys, and
the accuracy of their work is remarkable. They have thus
far been busy restoring the old types of things, which
involves very accurate labour, and among their interesting
jobs was the restoration of the famous Gog and Magog
clock which for more than a century hung in Cheapside,
London. We acquired it as a noteworthy example of in-

genious clock making. Two great figures, Gog and Magog, stand by the clock dial and, with swinging hammers, strike the hours and their divisions on big bells. We shall mount the clock in the village when it is completed.

You see, we are somewhat old-fashioned. That older, experienced worker alongside the boys, why, that is the way it was when I learned my trade. Boys ought to have older men to teach them: experienced craftsmen ought always to be teaching boys their craft. It is the natural way. We have assembled experience here, both living and as enshrined in objects.

This, however, is only one division of the work. In the Menlo Park laboratory, using the first floor only, for the second floor will be preserved as it was when Mr. Edison invented the electric light, several young men are working on the very practical problem of the extraction of low-grade iron ore. It is not now economical to use the low-grade iron ores because transporting them to the smelters costs too much. One of these days we shall be compelled to turn to the low-grade ores and then we shall need a method of getting the iron out of the ore right at the mine. On this the students are making considerable progress. In the grist mill another group of boys is learning to grind flour and others will learn baking and cooking. In the little frame building where Mr. Edison had his first bulbs blown—because he could not buy them anywhere—other boys are learning the arts of the glass blower and so on through a long list of village industries. The design is to rotate the boys through all of these various branches of fundamental industries in order to

give a comprehensive and practical background of knowledge and also to give the opportunity for a boy to find
out what he is best fitted to do, as well as what he most
likes to do. He learns a large section of history by learning something at first hand of every art through the ages.

The more a boy or a man knows, the more chance he
has to become a leader and, with everything at hand to
be seen, felt, and worked with, most certainly the road
to knowledge can be shortened. I know this from experience, for when I built my first motor car I had to dig
out every part and material for myself. There was no one
place I could go to and learn all that was to be had. Mr.
Edison had exactly the same trouble in his earlier days
of invention.

All of the boys in the Institute will spend their time
at useful and interesting work, and for it they are paid
at current rates, so that they are entirely self-supporting.
The present group of students has been variously selected.
They range from seventeen to nineteen years of age.
Some of them came from the trade schools, several from
the Wayside Inn school, and others from the outside. They
are only the nucleus of the eventual group, but we have
not decided—and we may never decide—how many will
be in this final group. There will be no fixed course. Some
of the more promising boys may stay well into manhood
in order further to develop themselves or to carry forward
work in which they are interested and which holds promise. Others may graduate into our own industries, while
still others may go outside. We do not try to hold men

whom we train: we are glad to see them dispersed throughout industry. We want here the freedom of the old university in which the scholars were presumed to be there because they wanted to learn something and not because their parents sent them. And as for leaders, we are taking for granted that they will be recognized as they appear, for there will be an entire freedom in the development of individuality.

The Henry Ford Trade School at the Highland Park plant was incorporated in 1916 and was the first step taken toward the working out of the general plan of education which culminates in the Edison Institute. It now has more than a thousand pupils and usually has a waiting list of around five thousand. It has graduated ten thousand young men. The original thought in this school and the thought that carries through all our feeder or elementary schools is to give an opportunity to the boy whom circumstances would otherwise force out into the world to earn an untrained living—and unless a boy be trained he cannot expect to get adequate wages. This is not an apprentice school nor is it a trade school in the usual sense. It is a school in which academic training and industrial instruction go hand in hand. The boys range from thirteen to eighteen. They spend one week in the classroom, where they are given instruction in the usual elementary school subjects. Then they spend two weeks in the school shops working under competent scientific instruction, with the most modern machinery, on practical articles for the account of the Ford Motor Company.

The plan is best illustrated by the school at the River Rouge plant, which is some three years old and which contains about a thousand students. The very young boys are not taken in at this school and, although the pupils receive elementary school instruction, they also progress into mechanical drawing, design, and various engineering subjects. Their shop work is very closely connected with that of the motor company itself. They are in the plant and not apart from it, and yet not a part of it—they are rather learning from the plant as a whole, though remaining in their own part of the plant. We are experimenting with keeping them in the plant and in the atmosphere of work rather than putting them into a separate building. They have their own shops and in these they work side by side with a few older experienced mechanics to the end of gaining a mastership of the hand and eye. They get insight into the finer departments of industry, by dealing with various kinds of measuring devices and the extremely delicate and accurate heads of fine turret lathes, in addition to many other methods of attaining precision. They learn the most accurate and painstaking forms of hand work as well as how to use modern tools. As they progress in skill and in age, they are advanced in responsibility and are given more and more the benefit of association with exceptionally well-skilled and experienced master craftsmen.

None of the products of either trade school is useless. Every item has to do with work that the Ford Motor Company requires to have done, and this work is paid

for by the company at current rates and is accepted only after the most rigid inspection. The trade schools are in the position of outside contractors and no favours are asked for or received by either side. The revenues from this work make both the schools entirely self-supporting. The boys work or study—they are both the same here— through an eight-hour day. The students are supported by a scholarship allowance which supports them while they are preparing themselves to be useful citizens. Under sixteen years, the scholarship amounts to twenty cents an hour, at sixteen it advances to twenty-five cents, at seventeen to thirty cents, and at eighteen to thirty-five cents. In addition to the scholarships, each boy receives his luncheon free and two dollars a month which he must deposit in a savings account. The record of each boy is taken every six weeks and, according to his record, the hourly value of his scholarship is advanced from one to three cents. The boys do all the work of their school. They perform the janitor service, keep the place painted and repaired, and cook and serve the meals.

The school at the Wayside Inn is of much the same character but its atmosphere is more generally agricultural. Since there is no great machine shop available to the students there, most of the craft work is in repair and outside construction. They have, under supervision, built a grist mill and will do whatever construction work is required in the further development of this particular school. And, as in the other schools, the boys are paid and fully earn their wages and their keep. The schools

we erect in various parts of the country will naturally take their character from the native tendency and needs, whether industrial or agricultural.

It will be seen, therefore, that first of all a boy is taught that which will enable him to earn his living and at the same time he is given enough academic training so that he can go as far in his book studies as he likes. He is not simply trained to be a mechanic. We are not producing machine men: we are producing self-sustaining citizens. These are not schools which are designed to keep up a supply of workmen for the Ford industries or any other industries. The young men who complete their courses and want to go to work can always find jobs in our industries, but that is far from being the purpose of the education. We emphasize the trade side only to make certain that the boy who leaves us will at the least have the ability to support himself. If he shows more ability than that, then the way to the Institute is open and he can go as far as he likes—or as far as his ability will carry him. At no stage will his education stop through lack of money—for he earns as he goes.

We hope by these means to evolve an education which will make both for invention and for leadership. A boy who can know what has been done in the past in the way of invention and design, not simply by reading about it but by seeing and working with the actual objects and machines, ought in a short time to acquire a knowledge such as could not otherwise be given. He can take advantage of all the experience that has gone before and, with this start, his mind should be so opened that it will

be bound to produce many new ideas. These new ideas may result in creating a new race of industrial leaders.

Most certainly we need leaders who know the past as something to learn from—and not as something to be bound by.

CHAPTER XIX

PROHIBITION OR POVERTY?

PROHIBITION is a moral issue. For it is economically right. We now know that anything which is economically right is also morally right. There can be no conflict between good economics and good morals. In fact the one cannot exist without the other.

For instance, it used to be believed that high wages were economically unsound—that, however desirable they might be, Nature had ruled otherwise. It was thought that the Lord had ordained that a certain portion of the people must always work for low wages—be slaves in all but name. For was it not plain that, if they received high wages, then goods would cost so much that only the very rich could buy them? It was the duty of the poor to stay poor and it was the duty of the rich to give them charity. The whole scheme sounded wrong. And it was wrong.

It has been demonstrated that poverty is not a natural state for anyone but is a condition brought about by bad management. We have learned that the only way to obtain really cheap goods is to pay high wages and get the most out of the wages by intelligence in management. Low wages, it has been proven, were never economically sound. No one has ever contended that they were morally desir-

able. Paying high wages is not to-day the evidence of a charitable mind. It is merely the evidence of possessing ordinary common sense. The best way of doing business is also the moral way.

The system of doing business with high wages and low prices may be called the American system, and since the coming of Prohibition it has welled up so much prosperity that some could not stand it. They made fools of themselves—just as certain kinds of people always do when they come quickly into a degree of wealth.

And thus, although to-day we are just as prosperous as we were last year, we are not quite as prosperous as we were two years ago. This recession has been taken advantage of by those who would destroy the prosperity of the people once and for all to stage a very active campaign to end Prohibition and bring back liquor. Our present industrial system simply cannot work with liquor. The executive who drinks cannot so plan that high wages will result in low prices, while the workman who drinks cannot work intelligently enough to earn high wages. We must choose between drink and poverty on the one hand and Prohibition and prosperity on the other. That is the choice. There is no middle ground. Look at our present situation.

This country has had a temporary set-back in its prosperity. There is no point in dodging that fact. But we have it in our own hands to determine whether we shall continue to slide back or whether we shall stop where we are and go forward again. The people did not move to check their prosperity. The people never move of themselves. They follow their leaders. Many of the men who

T

should have been leading toward a greater and more widely distributed prosperity took their minds off their real work and turned to gambling in the stock market. Many foolish people following these leaders also took to gambling. Those who won and lost large sums of money now find themselves too bewildered to get down to real, solid work. That is to say, the country has been prosperous since booze went out, but for the last two or three years we have had a money drunk.

This does not much matter. Leaders come and leaders go. Some men who have great capacity for leadership and who show the best that is in them during adversity are quite frequently unable to stand prosperity. They do not understand that the accumulation of riches is only a detail in the life of a real leader—that it merely marks a stage of progress and is not something to celebrate. It marks the beginning of a period when one should be able to be more useful than before. It is not the start of a vacation. Successful business endeavour has to be marked by something more than a pile of money. If it produces only money, then it is not of much importance—for anyone who is intent enough can make at least some money.

The great job which now confronts the leaders of industry is to learn enough about the processes of industry to keep the machines of the country going, not as in a boom but in a steady, progressive fashion so that prosperity will gradually seep through the whole country. One of the methods of doing this is to keep wages high and prices low, for then we not only give people the money with which to buy, but also, at the same time, through the low prices, give them the ability to buy more. Raising wages and at the same time raising prices is a meaningless gesture as far as prosperity is concerned, while lowering wages and also lowering prices leaves things exactly as they were before. Lowering wages and raising prices is the quickest and surest method of insuring the continuance of bad times. But raising wages and at the same time lowering prices calls for a great deal more than good intentions. It calls for every bit of brains that one can muster, for the margins of profit are made so narrow that they will disappear entirely unless every leader and supervisor, as well as every man engaged in the manual work, contributes all the keenness he possesses. There can be no let-down and no shirking.

The brain of a man who drinks alcohol cannot be wholly quick and alert. This is not to say that everyone who does not drink alcohol is quick and alert. But in these days a man needs all the brains he can command, and, whatever be the grade of those brains, they will be several grades lower if their owner drinks. I have not drunkards in mind. The drunkard is in the way of being an invalid and needs skilled medical care as greatly as though he were suffering from any other malignant disease. A nation of drunkards would not have to bother about its progress—there would be no progress to bother about. I am concerned with the man who drinks so moderately that he rarely feels its effects and therefore believes that liquor does not harm him—in fact, he becomes indignant at the very suggestion that it might hurt him.

My experience has been that there can be no temporizing whatsoever with liquor. We must have men who can and will use all the brains they possess. Therefore, since the very beginning, we have in our industries enforced the rule of absolute, total abstinence, both in and out of the shops and offices. We have applied this rule without exception, both to executives and to men and in every country in which we operate. We made this rule not merely because we are opposed to the drinking of liquor but because we are opposed to the cultivating of poverty.

The kingdom of poverty is very strongly fortified. It can be conquered only through making industry serve the whole people. We are all very far as yet from achieving this service, but since Prohibition came to this country we have made more rapid strides toward bringing industry around to the real service of humanity than we made during all the previous history of the world. When this service is perfected, we shall have made prosperity universal and have abolished poverty. The nation cannot go forward on this programme—which is the finest of all programmes—unless it has a full complement of brains and initiative. The nearer we approach national total abstinence, the more brains and initiative we shall have at command.

Brains and initiative are dulled by even the occasional use of alcohol. They are made permanently dull by even the most moderate habitual use, and they vanish altogether in the steady, heavy drinker. This is not my opinion out of hand and without regard to the facts. It is founded on the experience of many years of dealing with hundreds of thousands of men comprising all grades of capability from the highest to the lowest. I do not have to inquire whether or not a man is drinking after hours. I can learn everything I need to know just by talking to him about his section of the business. When an executive who has been very keen and capable begins to accept things as they are and to contribute no new, worthwhile ideas whatsoever, I can feel very certain that he is tippling out of hours. I can feel certain because in my experience it has been demonstrated that hardly one per cent of the letdowns in the man who is physically well is due to any cause other than drinking. I have seen a man taking only one or two glasses of wine a day on the advice of his doctor so change mentally as to be useless. Alcohol kills the will power. More than once I have had to remove men whom I greatly liked and respected and who had been very capable just because they decided that a very little liquor out of hours would do them good. I have had to remove them or give them long vacations, not because they were drinking but because they lacked the keenness which their jobs required. Brains and booze will not mix.

Among workmen this condition is not less apparent. To-day's manufacturing requires quick, precise work that calls on the brains far more than on the muscles. We have left behind us the time when most men were only so much beef and brawn and were needed only for their strength and endurance. Even in those days the man who did not drink always had more endurance than the man who did, but with nearly everyone drinking, the exceptional man who did not drink never had much of a chance, for his fellows resented his abstinence. In the class of skilled workmen, the differences became more apparent and always the teetotaller was preferred in employment above the drinker of approximately the same ability. I noted that very early in my own working days.

When I began to manufacture, I surrounded myself with men who did not drink. We had very little money to spend and we could not afford to waste any of it on men who could not be relied on to be always capable of giving their best. We had to watch every penny. As our operations grew and we took on more men, we kept to the same rule just as a matter of course, for a drinking man never seemed to fit. It was not necessary to ask a man whether or not he drank. The man who drank always stood out among his fellows who did not drink—he never did his work so well. If he did not show in his work that he had stopped drinking, then we simply let him go. More often we did not have to enforce the non-drinking rule. It rather enforced itself; the men quickly found out that they could not drink and do their work, so they either stopped drinking or quit. Thus gradually we gathered a force in which the drinkers were very few and all were transients on the way out. It was because we had such a force that back in 1915 we were able to raise our minimum wage to five dollars a day. We could not have paid that wage to a body of drinking men. We could not have paid that wage to a body of sober men if our executives had been drinkers. We were able to pay the wages and prosper exceedingly because everyone concerned was free from the hindrance of liquor.

As the years have passed, the work in our shops has become finer and has called for an increasing amount of skill and intelligence. A man who is working at a machine which is achieving an accuracy of a thousandth of an inch or better needs a keen brain. He needs a fine coördination between hand and brain even if he be only slipping a bolt through a hole. With a trained coördination every job becomes easy—almost effortless. But any use of alcohol at all seems to destroy that exact coördination, and the result is either slow work or spoiled work—or both. And always the work seems hard. The tippler has no great interest in his work. We rarely have to discharge the drinkers. They discharge themselves—a man will not stick at a job on which he is falling down.

We have factories in England, Ireland, France, and in many other countries which do not have Prohibition and there we pay wages on American standards of purchasing power—wages which commonly are far above the current rates. But we do not pay these wages to men who drink. We find that we cannot pay them, and the men who work for us accept the conditions without question. They do not drink, for they have found, just as our American workmen have found, that they cannot otherwise do their work and earn their wages. They choose to keep their jobs and give up their liquor. The exceptions are negligible.

Our workmen in Ireland, for example, are as sober as the soberest group one ever saw in America. We do not interfere with the politics of drink. England is curbing it in the best way for England. Belgium is curbing it in the best way for Belgium. I am only saying that we cannot pay American wages except where we have American sobriety.

High-wage industry has to be intelligent from top to bottom and there is absolutely no place in it for the drinking man. If liquor should return—and of course there is no danger of that—then this industrial system we have built up would break down. It could not continue to pay high wages and sell goods cheaply, and for several reasons. First, the efficiency of both management and men would so drop that the high wages would result in dear goods instead of in cheap goods. That would at once restrict the markets. Second, if the people spent a part of their money for drink, then that much purchasing power would be withdrawn from the general market. Third, with the higher prices and lower purchasing power, the volume markets on which industry depends would vanish. Fourth, without these volume markets there could be no really big business and, since only big business can pay the highest wages, we should begin to slump back and be compelled to figure on how little men could be hired to work for instead of, as now, figuring how much we can pay to them.

Under such circumstances I, for one, should not want to continue in business. There would be nothing ahead worth achieving. Working just to get more money is out of the question.

And this is quite aside from the fact that our life

to-day, outside the shops and the offices, is so geared that a drinking man is a menace.

The inevitable consequence of small-scale production is poverty, for if only a small amount of wealth be produced, then there will be only a small pot to divide and everyone's rations will be short. There is no getting away from this. No method can be devised to distribute what is not there to distribute. Prohibition has made it possible for the nation to create a bigger pot of goods than ever before and therefore to have more to distribute and therefore to that extent to drive back the poverty line.

President Hoover has pledged himself to take every step toward the abolishing of poverty. There can be no lessening of poverty unless the Prohibition laws be observed with the most conscientious honesty as anti-poverty laws, the violation of which makes only for human misery. We need that viewpoint. The criminals who wreck banks or peddle narcotics do not create more misery and do not more deeply hurt society in general than the men who bootleg booze. It is wrong, to my mind, to speak of "enforcing" the Prohibition laws as though they were laws imposed by force upon the people and without their consent. These laws were made by the people for their own protection and the people will support the President to any length to which he may find it necessary to go to see that these laws are obeyed and the criminal booze element driven out.

Ours is a highly intelligent people. They are not in the least fooled by the tremendous and well-financed propaganda which hopes to break down Prohibition,

destroy prosperity, and reëstablish poverty as an institution. The people very well remember just how much the
liquor interests in the old days thought of the welfare of
the people and also they remember how many politicians
these interests then had at their beck and call. A great
many are now wondering whether all the old connections
have as yet been severed.

The number of people who are being honestly deluded
concerning the sentiment of this country on the Prohibition
question is very small. The anti-Prohibitionists make a
great deal of noise but it will be noted that it is always the
same people making the same noise. They are really only
a stage army marching into the wings and out again. And
this a number of politicians will very shortly have brought
home to them.

For Prohibition, as the great intelligent rank and file
of our people fully realize, marks the opening of the way
toward economic liberty. That is the only true liberty;
without it no other kind of liberty matters. It would seem
that those who would block the road to liberty and attempt
to substitute for true liberty the slavery of alcohol would
feel upon them the weight of a great responsibility. Those
who profess so much concern for the workingman that
they would start him drinking again care about as much
for him as a dog does about his forty-seventh grand-dad.

This Prohibition question is dynamite. The people established it without the help and against the opposition of
the whole race of politicians. We are only now getting
an occasional public official who is sincerely and person-

ally in favour of Prohibition. Until the whole political personnel is made over, a difference will seem to exist between the people and their officials. But in the meantime, if any public official wants to discover what dynamite is, let him try to hinder Prohibition.

CHAPTER XX

MOVING FORWARD

THIS has been a record of experience.

Perhaps out of this experience may be gained some knowledge of these changing times, for the lessons which we have learned and the new horizons which we have discerned hold more than a private or local meaning.

The cure for that which is wrong must be found in moving forward away from the wrong. It is never possible to go back to anything. This is very fortunate, for if we could go back we should find at our journey's end a condition of affairs very much worse than that from which we thought we were escaping. Things are better to-day than they were yesterday. They can be made better to-morrow than they are to-day. It is not necessary to be either an optimist or a pessimist. It is enough to move forward with what intelligence we can give to the day's work.

For instance most of the theories as to the place of machinery in modern life—of what machinery is and does —seem to be based on almost everything except an actual observation of machinery and its effects. There is a great deal of writing, a small amount of thinking, and almost no seeing at all.

Take some of the more current delusions:

Machinery is labour saving, and hence it displaces men and robs them of their right to work.

Machinery calls for no skill on the part of the worker and gradually makes him a dull, heavy being without the power of thought.

Machinery fills the world with goods and puts all of the power in the hands of those who own the machinery, for they can cut off the supply at any time they wish.

Machinery makes for ugly products and so we have an ugly world which promises to grow uglier.

Machinery has taken away liberty as well as leisure and will in time change the human being into some kind of machine.

Machinery is a curse, and we really ought to get rid of it or at least confine its use within reasonable bounds.

It is perfectly true that some kinds of machinery do displace men, and if that were the only sort of machinery there would be no work for men. But then also there would be no work for the machines. For the machines presumably exist to produce goods in large quantities, and if they could do that without human aid, the customers for their production would be so few that the machines could not be continued in operation. The big customers of industry are the wage earnes.

To worry about the approach of that day when all industry will be on so complete a machine basis that workmen will have no place in the scheme is to worry about an utter absurdity. There are quite a number of ultimate happenings that we do not have to bother about. There used to be a deal of concern as to what would happen if the sun should suddenly stop giving out heat. That would be an unfortunate event, but it is nothing to worry over—for we can do not a single thing about it.

The great corporation still makes many people anxious —although the corporations of to-day are many times larger than the corporations which started the anxiety. Monopoly, we now know, is impossible, for the reason that a monopoly based on anything but service is self-destructive. It throws away its customers as it goes along. That has been demonstrated time and again. Centralization may degenerate into monopoly, but proper centralization means higher service.

In the catalogue of modern delusions is one to the effect that the United States is invading the whole world with its products in a vast attempt to own the world. This notion arises from the old way of thinking, in which it was taken for granted that there was only so much of anything to go around and that the big question was how to divide the contents of the pot. The business of the United States can succeed abroad only for the same reasons for which it succeeds at home—by filling a need not otherwise satisfied and by creating the purchasing power of the people to buy the goods. The amount of goods which American industry can sell abroad is not of much importance in the general scale of our industry. The American cannot benefit at the expense of the foreigner. He cannot take away the wealth of the foreigner. For one thing, there is not enough of it. American business abroad must create its customs by becoming a part of the wealth-producing machinery of the country.

Americans are not invading; they are returning home from their journeys. The sons who came out from the British Isles and the continent of Europe as pioneers in a new world are taking back home the ideas that they have learned in their pioneering.

It is often said that the tastes of the public change and that a manufacturer must keep up with them. But it would seem rather to be the other way about. For in those countries where the manufacturers preserve their machinery with the care that we give to antiques the tastes of the public do not change—people keep on asking for exactly the same sort of articles year after year. A fair part of the world is living exactly as it did in the Middle Ages. Articles which are made by hand do not greatly vary through the years. It would seem that the manufacturer and not the public is responsible for the changes in taste.

What is a manufacturer? He is both a clearing house and a manager of ideas, machinery, material, and men. He may also be an inventor—but that is a side separate from his actual manufacturing. If he is not an inventor, he uses the inventions of others in turning out goods or articles which someone has invented—although the actual article, as for instance a stocking, may have been invented so many years ago that we no longer think of it as invention. If he pushes his business, he will continually be finding new and better ways of making his product. And thus in the course of time he will by better manufacturing teach the public to demand more service than before. Also he will himself have learned so much that he can turn out a product which will meet the new demand for service.

The changes thus come about through the amount of science that the manufacturer puts into his work. This pressure to do a better job is very different from making a new style just for its own sake or to hoodwink people into imagining that what they have is obsolete. A business can be quickly destroyed by superseding one product by another which is no better, merely to induce fresh buying. This is breaking faith with the public. For a while the public may not feel that its confidence has been violated. But in the end it will find out—and it will cease to buy. For no manufacturer makes anything for which the public cannot find a satisfactory substitute.

A business, just like a piece of machinery, has to be in balance, and this balance means more than keeping production in line with consumption, or seeing to it that supplies are on hand so that there will never be too little or too much, or seeing to it that there is always enough money on hand to pay wages and bills and to make changes or extensions as and when they are needed. There is a larger balance than this, and that is the balance of prices, profits, and wages; and, naturally, if a business tries to regulate any of these factors by what other businesses are doing, the balance will be thrown out.

Normal and growing business requires constant control of profits by diverting a portion of them into lowering prices or increasing wages or both. We have been doing this right along, but every time we lower prices or increase wages the profits also increase. For the pressure brings about lower costs; the lowering of prices and the raising of wages increase the buying and therefore the volume of production—which makes possible further economies—the men work with more interest, and all the factors combine to increase profits again. We plan the price as a part of the design of the product. For instance, in designing Model A we had in mind all that we had learned with Model T in respect to price, simplicity, and durability. We knew that there was a large public need for an automobile at approximately the same price as Model T, but that it had to be a very much faster, better looking, and more comfortable car than Model T, while at the same time retaining all the features of durability and freedom from repair. When the design was finally finished—or rather when the car was ready for production, for the design will never be fully completed —we arranged our prices on what, out of our experience, we thought the car ought to be made for. The first hundred thousand cars cost more than we sold them at. The loss on the next hundred thousand was smaller and by the time we had reached half a million we had a satisfactory profit. This profit has increased on each hundred thousand, so that the losses on the earlier cars have been much more than made up.

This is not a guessing at price or anything of the sort. It is merely making price a part of the design. In designing a motor, for instance, one settles upon an exact cylinder size so that the motor will exert a certain power. Each part of the motor has to be of a size and strength to fit in with this scheme. There are limitations on the design; it is perfectly possible to design a motor that we could not build in quantity, and also it would be very easily possible to design a motor that we could build in quantity and which would be

U

a very good motor but would be very difficult indeed to adjust or repair. Price must enter into the design just as much as the bore of the cylinder. Price is an integral part of the scheme of manufacturing.

Before making even a minor change in design, let alone a complete change, we build a great number of experimental cars, for after we have used all of the theory and experience at our command we check and recheck by actual performance. The building of these experimental cars is very expensive. They do not give us a line on costs—and anyhow we regard costs as flexible and not as binding—but these experiments do give us a fairly close idea of what we should be able to do on a production of a certain size. For instance, on Model A we fixed our prices on a production of around two million cars a year, with the full knowledge that probably we should produce several hundred thousand cars at more than the sales price, but also with the firm belief, based on our past experience, that in the course of time we should make a profit on the price. If we had failed to learn to make the car for the price we fixed, then we should have known that we had designed the wrong kind of car. For, to repeat, the price was part of the design. As it actually turned out, we began to earn a profit much earlier than we had expected.

To me this method of including the price in the design is the really scientific method. What is the use of designing a piece of machinery and then having its manufacture cost so much that the people for whose use it is designed will not have the money to buy it? As one progresses in the manufacturing, and as costs become lower, it is extremely bad business not to lower the price. This may be done in two ways. The first is by so improving the quality that the purchaser will get more for his money, and the second is by actually lowering the price. But it is not enough to do only the one or the other. More and more quality and workmanship must be built into the product, and whenever there is a question between raising the quality and lowering the price it is better to raise the quality, for then one will shortly be able to lower the price anyway.

There is no question at all that so-called periods of extravagance on the part of the people are artificially induced. They originate in the minds of those who wish to speed up the people's spending. There is no dangerous business practice in existence to-day that was not deliberately taught or forced upon the people by men who had no thought of the general social benefit.

Teaching and leading the people to invest wisely, to begin getting things that make their lives more productive of real values, is one thing. Teaching them to forget their natural abhorrence of debt, leading them to forego their independence by working for a small army of installment collectors, is quite another thing. Extreme thrift bordering on miserliness is a greater social evil than free spending. The point is not in the spending. It is on the purpose of the spending. And a business which urges unwise buying is in danger. The self-limited business can weather any gale, but vast edifices built on a gamble in the people's extravagance must collapse.

Any business is precarious that tries to force people into buying its products or that tries to make sales to customers who are already well provided for. Any business that misrepresents its product is certainly in very great danger. The misrepresentation may take many forms. One of the most common is to misrepresent a rival manufacturer's product in the hope that the buyer will then have more money with which to buy yours. These practices all spring from the same thought that the people have only so much to spend and that business is a scramble to get first to a limited number of dollars. That is not business at all and cannot have permanency. If what are called the selling expenses of a product are high in proportion to its price then there is something very wrong with the product.

The purpose of any business is to supply human needs, and when that purpose has been accomplished the business for the time being is through. If the human needs change— and they are changing all the while—then the business, unless it adapts itself to the new needs, is through and done for. Its further continuance is an economic waste. It is part of business—the biggest part—to give service. When there is only a known and well-defined service to be given, the limits of a business have been reached. As long, however, as there is service to be improved the possibilities of expansion are present.

Two normal periods of rest in business are, first, when the supply of services or goods is sufficient for the time, and, second, when the progress of the concern represents the utmost vision of its managers up to the moment. These breathing periods come naturally and should not be described as panics. A man is not in a panic because he slows up for an afternoon. American business has as little scientific knowledge of panics as it has of prosperity, and if it had more scientific knowledge of prosperity there would be less need of experience with panics. But this much should be clear, even to professional economists, that a breathing spell is not ominous. It is indeed normal and wholesome, and not to be treated by the injection of stimulants.

This is not at all to say that business cannot be made more regular by some kind of authority from a central power—for instance the government. There are times when wise governmental expenditure in the provision of wealth-creating enterprises such as roads, waterways, and flood prevention may serve to help some temporary condition, but the real regulation must come from within business itself. If the public can be worked up to reckless spending and if business men take advantage of this state of mind— for which as a rule they are responsible—to give less than full value, then inevitably there will be a reaction against all purchasing. And, likewise, whenever a business finds that it is giving less than full value or the wrong kind of value, then it is time for that business to withdraw and put itself in order, for in neither case is it engaged in an essential service. One of the very large objections to any kind of government ownership or regulation is a lack of flexibility. Bureaucrats tend to enforce a rule or to continue a style long after the need has ceased.

No business can truly be regarded as an institution in the sense that it can continue forever without changing its policy, its product, and even its very form. Both industry and men in these days have to be very mobile in order to be prosperous—which is only another way of saying in order to give service. There are no unchanging essential industries. An essential industry is one, the products of which help the individual to a freer life. The essentials of yesterday are not the essentials of to-day. The mining of coal was once an essential industry. It still is—but in a fashion quite different from formerly. A modern household should not to-day need any coal, but industry needs more coal than ever before. The household pump was once an essential; now it has been supplanted by the central water systems in the towns and cities. On any farm where much water is needed the hand pump is a waste. These shiftings are constant and inevitable. It is only when they are not recognized and stimulants are applied to cure what is really a constitutional defect that we have periods of depression.

If every business kept informed as to its own condition and paid no attention at all to that unreal thing known as the "general state of business," then, although a business here might be up and another business there might be down, the average of prosperity could be maintained. There is no business cycle. Periods of general depression come about solely through a lack of intelligence on the part of industrial and financial leaders.

Prosperity itself is only a relative term. It merely expresses the fact that to-day's average is better than yesterday's. We have not as yet gained a really universal prosperity in the United States, although we are heading that way. It is within our reach, and of course it involves the abolition of poverty.

Considered on the whole we are to-day prosperous. But prosperity cannot be considered as achieved unless it reaches to all parts of this country and to all classes. And we shall not be able to raise our own prosperity to that point without also raising that of the world.

CHAPTER XXI

THE LIMITS OF MONEY

THE great monotony is to be found not in work but in poverty. No mechanical operation can be devised, no form of employment can be devised, which can equal in blankness the leaden dullness of continuous poverty. The only monotony which can approach that of poverty is the monotony of stagnant wealth. To remove the causes of poverty is a job which cannot in the smallest degree be dodged or glossed over. It cannot be met by smart sayings; it must be met only by work.

And the tendency is to lose the perspective upon our work and think that we may somehow escape from it. But work is the essential. Without it there is nothing. Work determines a man's place in the world; it indicates the calibre of his mind and character and expresses the measure of his usefulness to his fellow men.

The only justification for education is that it fits a man for work—directly for the special work which he plans to do or indirectly by tempering and edging the tools of his intellectual equipment. The separation of education from work is now recognized as a false step. The white collar is ceasing to be the badge of intelligence. The theory that education has as its proper end the providing of a detour around work is no longer tenable. The world needs leaders, and the first qualification of a leader is the ability himself to do whatever he may require to be done by his command. The world has more than enough clerks who record other men's work. The need is for workers, not only to work at the job to which they are set, but to work at work itself —at wages, finance, distribution, and the rest of the great problem. Everything, it is said, ought to be easy. Work that amounts to anything will never be easy. The hardest work we do is also the most important thing we do—the work of thinking. The higher one goes in the scale of responsibility, the harder the job becomes. The work of thinking cannot be delegated.

Ease has its place. Every man who works hard ought to have sufficient leisure. No one deserves ease—indeed, no one can appreciate ease—except the one who works.

But it will never be possible to import comfortable and upholstered ease into work. Easy work is a contradiction in terms. Some work is needlessly hard, but that is because not enough thought has been put into it by the manager who planned it. It can be eased by proper management. Every device ought to be procured to leave a man free to do a man's work. Flesh and blood should not be made to bear burdens that steel can bear. But even when the best is done, work still remains work, and any man who puts himself into his job will feel that it is work. It is this which causes him to appreciate leisure.

Through work may come the escape from pure materialism. There are indications of that already.

Because the original motive which bound man to labour was the need for physical sustenance, it has been assumed that this constitutes the only meaning which labour can have for man. There comes a time, however, when the normal sense of acquisitiveness is satisfied and individuals begin to ask what progress is worth, and what it all means. This challenge arises most readily in American life. For here we have the tradition of work, in contrast to the tradition of acquiring a fortune in order to retire from work. We feel here that work is so large a part of a man's life that he cannot relinquish it without at the same time relinquishing a part of his life.

When the work happens to be, as in America, highly profitable and surrounded by an atmosphere of plenty in every field—plenty of material, plenty of jobs, plenty of wages, plenty of business, plenty of capital, and plenty of profits—in short all that of which impoverished men think they would never grow tired, it is not strange to see stagnation occur, which is first of all, perhaps, a stagnation of interest. Let us put it this way: Why all the rush and activity? Answer: to keep the wheels turning. Why all these wheels turning? Answer: to keep business going. Now, unless the answer is that we are serving life and deepening experience, there is no answer at all. Stagnation of interest comes when we fail to see where work and business actually serve life.

For there are two things of which men grow weary in the material sphere—meaningless poverty and meaningless prosperity. It is simply that a dominant condition at either extreme of the scale of goods becomes tiresome unless something else is added to it. The fact is that both poverty and plutocracy are insufferably dull.

Sometimes the people simply grow tired of merely being busy and prosperous, for even business and prosperity lose their savour if they are nothing more than what we usually mean by these terms. The economist has never taken into account the possibility of people growing tired of mere business and mere prosperity.

The phenomenon of stagnation amid plenty has been growing. We are learning that the game of business will not play itself, that the players of business will not keep playing when their interest flags, that it seems to be a law that interest flags in proportion to the lowness of the purposes involved. Selfishness is the least sustaining interest in the world. As a motive power for continuous effort and increasingly refined effort it fails miserably.

Above a certain grade of income, money alone will not draw out a man's best work. The opposite of this is not true. That is to say, there are no stages in which money may be disregarded as a reward for work, or at least it cannot be disregarded by the one who directs the work and profits by it. The substitute for money as a reward for work will not be found in the provision of toys and childish games masquerading as incentives and usually designed to take the worker's mind off the fact that he is getting less money for his work than he ought to be getting. And neither will the substitute be found in creating some kind of an atmosphere of amiability and good-fellowship, which has as its end the pretending that work is not work.

It will be, as I see it, the duty of the leaders to work unceasingly, finding their satisfaction in their work and,

when, if ever, the times comes that they do not find satisfaction, then at once to retire and give way to those who do
find satisfaction. But all of this is in the future. It is a
pleasant sign that money is becoming less than the best
incentive in certain grades of work, but it is not yet time
to decide that money and the things which money buys are
not incentives. That would not be true. The world still
wants money, and it is going to continue that want until
it is completely surfeited. We gain nothing by a solemn
wagging of heads and spinning of theories. We can theorize
only by assuming that things will always remain as they
are—that all the tendencies which we note will be intensi-
fied. That is never the case. Our affairs in the future are
bound to be shaped as they have been in the past by forces
of which we to-day know nothing.

Take a simple illustration. Many years ago, before the
coming of the automobile, there was a great agitation in
this country about the necessity for building new roads
because at that time most of our roads were very bad indeed. The roads of Europe were very generally held up to
us as an example of what we should have here. It was not
recognized at all that conditions here were very different
from those in Europe, that the railroad was then our best
method of transportation, and that moving goods over even
the best of roads by horses was quite too slow for our needs.
The road enthusiasts insisted that we must have new high-
ways, and they had some very ingenious plans of finance.
But they did not make any progress, for they could not get
the people interested. It is very lucky that they could not,
for then we should have had the country cut up with a net-

work of roads quite unsuited to a method of transportation which was at the time unknown.

To-day we have a farming problem. It is being handled on the supposition that things will always remain as they are. There are suggestions of subsidizing the farmer with public funds. There are suggestions of making the whole matter turn on methods of marketing. There are suggestions of restricting the crops and using artificial tariff methods to keep an unnatural price level. All these plans are founded on the assumption that things are going to remain as they are—that the conditions of the world as they affect farming are fixed.

What is happening? In a few years, instead of finding means to stop the flow of grain into our country, we shall be calling upon the world for greater importation. The present solutions of marketing plans and financial aids will be swept away as the stagecoach disappeared before the railways. Agriculture is now becoming the basis of the new chemical era. What we have thus far done with coal tar we shall soon be doing with cellulose. The farms will be linked up with great industries, and a greater production and importation than we have dreamed will be necessary.

There will sometime be a solution of the money problem—though no one now sees just how it will come. But it must come. The very pressure of real wealth on the signs of wealth—that is, on money—will reform the money system into something bigger and more useful. The enemy of money is wealth, and wealth is gaining the ascendance over money.

On none of these points do we know enough to take action. Our present course is that ordained by experience, and the most useful thing that any of us can do is to put the results of our daily experience into our day's work. For then and only then can we be sure that we are really progressing.

MANKIND PASSES FROM THE OLD TO THE NEW ON A HUMAN BRIDGE FORMED BY THOSE WHO LABOUR IN THE THREE PRINCIPAL ARTS—AGRICULTURE— MANUFACTURE—TRANSPORTATION

THE END